the
sea
once
swallowed
me

**A MEMOIR
OF LOVE, SOLITUDE,
AND THE LIMITS
OF LANGUAGE**

by

Sondra

This is a work of creative nonfiction. I have tried to faithfully recreate events, locales, and conversations to the best of my memory's ability, though some thoughts and interpretations ascribed to the narrator (me) have been influenced by the few years of growth since the experiences. In order to maintain their anonymity, I have changed the names of most characters and may have changed some minor identifying characteristics and details.

Copyright © Sondra, 2021

ISBN: 978-1-7362320-1-9

All rights reserved. No part of this book may be reproduced in any form, by electronic or mechanical means, including information storage and retrieval systems, without permission in writing from the publisher, except by a reviewer who may quote brief passages in a review.

www.sondrawriter.com

I feed you these words
like shards of glass.
May they become
shards of light
as you swallow.

The boy with the dog has taken back his sleeping bag.

So I sit with my back against this tree, a tattered curtain wrapped around my body as the rain sifts through the leaves to soak me.

3 a.m.

I live in the trees outside a Medieval Catalan city.

Why?

Well, I would explain, but a stone has begun to distract me. It is pressed against the roots of the tree, sitting calmly as if it has something to say.

I narrow my eyes. *You don't belong here.*

It's smooth and veined with white quartz, like a stone washed up from the sea. But the cliffs of La Costa Brava are twenty miles from these woods. How long have you been inching across this dry earth, just to sit in front of me with your blue skin darkening, saying *see*?

The stone's white veins pulse gently in the moonlight; our shared cold begins to clatter in my teeth.

I am here to decipher nature, I think defiantly. But as the stone glints back, I know this is a lie. Humans can decipher nothing but their own small lives.

Then peace. If not wisdom, then—

But the words lay unfinished in my brain as I pull the curtain tighter around my body, my cheek pressed against the bark of the tree until it marks me.

In the morning, the sun shines manic as an apology.

Heat wrestles through the fabric until I untuck my head, throwing the curtain and tarp to one side. I palm hair from my face, surprised that the shade has deepened to the color of blood.

The rain, I remember. I look down at my body clothed in layers of damp. *Cold*. The sensation strikes as soon as the word forms, so I strip silently, laying my clothes over the tree's roots.

Leaves shiver in waves of morning breath, and I shiver too. Nearly naked, I am left in a beige bra and black underwear, my white skin prickling.

Inhale. Exhale. The sun slides over my goose-fleshed body, warming me. *This is life*, I think, my inner voice beginning to sermonize. *This is—*

I hear voices on the road beneath and hurry to my storage tree. I clear the vines and uncover the slab of wood, pulling out my daypack beneath. It's dry (this always surprises me, and a smile springs to my face). Inside the daypack, crammed beneath my laptop, is a bright magenta dress. It waves in the wind when I raise it to the light, the flowered fabric smoothing as I slip it over my body.

The voices are gone, so I scramble back to my sleeping spot and pull out my notebook. I lay on the tarp to let the morning sky seep through my skin. Before its bleached canvas is devoured by blue and pulses like a body in heat, the day hums open as a fresh page. *This* is my favorite time to write.

"*You*," I say, squinting into her electric absence of color.

The sky blinks back, blinded by her own white.

"You're the reason I'm here. I only write because I can't squeeze out your light and press it to a page. I am writing because the alternative is to stay stunned that I am alive."

She laughs. You know the sky is laughing when the blue begins to expand and contract, like an attack of the diaphragm.

My smile is wiped clean by this laugh. *I am ridiculous.*

I stand, throw the tarp and curtain over the bushes to dry, and tuck the notebook in my daypack. I will go to the library and write. I will write until I understand. I will write until meaning sinks into these pages like the sky sinks into the trees.

A story can begin anywhere. Its roots reach into my future as much as they dig into my past, and then further, into the deep past of centuries. But we must begin somewhere, so let us begin on a Tuesday in Vidreres, Spain.

I had been living with a Catalan family for a month, teaching the two daughters English. They were a loving family in a home filled with light. The light had a life of its own, glancing off the polished banisters, warming the turquoise and aquamarine mosaic tiling, laying in strips over the natural stone walls. You could follow it from room to room as it shape-shifted, eluded.

Each morning, I sat with the girls in the grass outside, playing English games and shaking my head when they spoke to me in Spanish. In the afternoons, we ate paella or pasta on the patio followed by fresh cubes of fruit. We'd go swimming in a nearby pool, drying ourselves and taking afternoon naps as the house shook with shadows, flickered with light.

Well, the family would nap—as sweetly and soundly as cats in a window—while I would write. The parents urged me to slow down and succumb to the siesta. It was hard not to, in the slumber-striking heat that filled my tiny room. I would draw the blinds, open my laptop on the desk and drink lemon-lime soda to keep me awake between sentences, between words.

A few times a week we would bring *bocadillos* and tortilla Española to the beach. The mother and her friends would lose their bikini tops and lay on their towels, chatting. The girls would run into the waves and I would sit in the water and stare at my feet, stunned by the colors of everything. The sea was like the mosaic tiles in their home, a thousand shades shattered and glued by light into the bounded bodies of waves. As they covered my toes and sunk under me, I found myself wishing I could stay. On this beach. In this city. Whatever it took to avoid the solitude that awaited me.

But the Tuesday of our beginning arrived, and I found myself giving hugs and saying my goodbyes. As I lingered awkwardly at the door, the mother slipped fifty euros into my palm, telling me to keep in touch.

I had lied. They thought I was going to France for another work exchange, but I was taking a bus to Girona, a city only twenty miles away. How could I explain my desire to sleep in the woods to these level-headed people? They had friends in Girona, friends I could have stayed with. Or I could have gone home.

But I could not have gone home. Not with my authenticity intact. Which is the point, I think. Learning from the trees, for whom authenticity is simple as breathing.

I hugged them each again, saying "thank you" and "I'll write you on Facebook," since I have no cellphone.

The morning is sickly for want of sun. I struggle beneath my pack as I walk to the Vidreres bus stop. And I see Makono for the first time, sitting on the bench and laughing at me.

"What?" I ask, having waddled to a stop in front of him.

"What a pack!" he exclaims.

He's right to laugh. Everything I own is wrapped in tarp and tied with rope into the shape of a pack. The straps are made of a small beige curtain I found in my garage the night before I left home. A homemade monstrosity. I had bought a smaller backpack the day before, and this I balanced lengthwise on top, my arms reaching over my head in order to stabilize.

"Yes," I agree, without laughing. I slide the packs off my back and sit beside him. After a moment's silence, I ask why he's headed to Girona.

He glances at me. "To visit my cousins."

I nod.

"And you?"

"I am going to meet the new family I'll be staying with," After a pause I add, "I'm teaching their daughters English."

"Ahh," he says.

When the bus pulls up, he stands and swings my packs over his shoulder. I see his height, his muscular arms flexing with the weight. "I got it," he insists, leading the way. He pays bus fare for the two of us and invites me to sit next to him.

I can see he is trying to impress me, but I can't be so paranoid about men that I refuse to make friends. "I'm from America," I say.

He draws back. "I thought you were a Spaniard."

"You only say that because *you're* not a Spaniard," I tease. He speaks with bad grammar but no embarrassment, like he's been successfully communicating with native speakers for years.

He smiles. "I'm from Mali. Do you know it?"

"It's in Africa," I respond, having no idea *where* in Africa.

"Yes," and he pulls out his smartphone, Googling a map. "Right beneath Algeria."

"Hmm," I say, and to expiate my ignorance, I ask about the culture.

He finds a video of an albino man singing a folk song, and we begin watching the concert. As he holds the screen between us, I turn my head to catch the gaze of an older woman across the aisle, an expression of distaste tensing her upper lip. I turn back to the screen, saying nothing.

"Ignore it," he says, nodding at her. "You're probably the first white girl she has seen talking to a black man."

I laugh uncomfortably. "Not possible."

He tucks his phone away and leans closer. "Listen. You're the first white woman who has had a conversation with me in the seven years I've lived here."

"No," I say, shaking my head. But I feel compelled to add, "You know Catalans are private. Don't take it personally."

"Oh, I don't. It's not about me. It's about my color."

I shake my head again, because I can say nothing. But I glance back at the woman and am shocked to see she is still staring. The unmistakable disdain still distorts her face as she locks into my gaze. She raises an eyebrow. I smile weakly and turn back to him.

"Yeah," I say, scratching my neck.

"Yeah," he replies.

When the bus pulls into a massive parking lot, he stands up with my pack. "I'll help you," he says, as we start filing out. I tell him I will be just fine, but he shakes his head, leading me to the station where there are storage lockers.

"Why do you need a locker?" he asks. "Aren't you going to a family's house?"

I feel annoyed by his intrusion, but I just shake my head. "I have to find it first. Then I'll come back."

He clicks his tongue, and I wonder if this means something in his native language, a hidden subtext I will never understand.

"I'll help you find the house," he offers, as we exit the bus station.

I look at the sky, hardening into a deep blue heat. I had searched Google Earth the night before so I know there are woods behind *la parte antigua* of the city, but I don't know how long it will take to find a decent place to sleep.

"Honestly," I state. "I'm fine."

"Then let me get you some food first," he says, "I'll walk you to a place."

I scan the streets vaguely, wondering if it's a good idea to waste another hour with a stranger who may or may not be hitting on me.

"Fine," I agree. "But I can't be long."

We walk to a small café where he orders me two sandwiches and himself half a chicken. He tells me more about Mali, and I tell him about my family. He seems nice enough, but I can't concentrate. All I can think about is how to escape, how to start looking for a camp spot before it gets dark. I pull out my laptop, pretending to check my email, and say, "Oh great, they just sent the address. I should head out."

He moves behind me to glance at it, but I stand and shut the laptop, turning to face him. "I got it."

"You know where it is?" he asks.

"*Claro*. It will be easy to find."

"Sit for a minute longer then." He nods to the chair and I sit down just long enough to gather my things. But he sits next to me and slips an arm around my shoulder.

"No," I say, rising to my feet. "Don't touch me."

He stands too. "Oh, I'm…I'm sorry."

"No, I've just…I've had bad experiences since I've been in Europe, and I'm not interested in anything romantic. We can be friends, but nothing more." And then I straighten a bit, reminding myself to be firm. "Do you understand?"

"Yes, yes, yes," and he looks genuinely upset. "I respect women," he says. "I always respect women. I don't want you to be uncomfortable."

And I am surprised, because I have never before said "no" and received an apology. I nod and grab my bags. "It's okay. Just wanted to let you know."

"Maybe..." he starts, "we can be friends. We can just be friends."

"Yeah, maybe when you come visit Girona," I say, but my thoughts are already in the woods; I am already forgetting him.

"Yes," he agrees, and I thank him for the food and say goodbye.

He was harmless, I think, as I walk away, pleased at my good judgment. And a good omen to begin this adventure on a full stomach. But I'm happy that he is going to his cousins' now, that maybe he will be back, but we will not likely cross paths again.

This book is already crammed with men, I think. *Where will I breathe if I let another in?*

By the time I arrive, the first garden is already rasping beneath the failing light. I sit on a bench, newly painted blue for the contemplation of weary tourists. I contemplate, I suppose. Or soak in its strangeness like a sponge.

The hum of decay is deafening. It textures the air with a loamy remembering. It must be the influence of these ruins that crumble around me, stone walls melting into dirt—*old bones, meet the older earth*. I am fascinated by their stillness.

Then I look at my feet and the grass beneath. The fast-decomposing light combs the slender blades with its fingers. Above me, dusk hazes the tree-heads with a diminuendo-shade of gold, like the sound of orchestral violins before a symphony's last gasp.

Beauty, like death, has a way of breaking through to our bodies. While beauty reminds us of our dwindling breath supply, death sweeps it up into the broader tide, the universal inaugurated by personal obliteration.

I am aware of my pulse throbbing through my neck, so I must be afraid. The world is starkening. The colors crispen. The grain of the wooden bench and the shimmering leaves are menacing in their clarity. *The day will soon be dead.*

Death shades the contours of life.

The first page of my notebook is crisp, waiting.

Which is why at the brink of death, everything becomes painfully alive—

I feel close to that. To the brink of something.

I imagine the Sondra of a few months ago, walking home from the university library as the sky splattered inky blues onto a moon-slicked pavement.

I place a pin in my head, highlighting the memory in red. *That.* That is why I came to Spain.

The sky.

While walking in the night after a day of studying philosophy, my thinking seemed to peel like paint from the walls of my brain, words and formulas tumbling to prostration before the ruthless purity of atmospheric light.

Her subtle dark pulsation felt truer than logic, truer than

$$\frac{\begin{array}{c} p \\ p \rightarrow q \end{array}}{\therefore q}$$

Unspeakable, she hovers over waters, sifts through wind-spoken leaves, and lands in the lungs like a long-lodged remembering.

Once singed by her authenticity, my life story seemed stamped with a scarlet letter. *Do I jump in bed with any societal script? Do I belong to my own words?* I wondered sometimes if anyone believed what they claimed. It seemed that beliefs were simply crumbs tossed to a hungry god of belonging, letter jackets donned for acceptance into polite society. Even the renegades followed a script which they themselves had not written, and "non-conformity" never reached deep enough to destabilize the dominant story. Professors, PhDs, intelligent dissenters—none of them were immune. Their words lacked substance; their eyes lacked life. *Did mine?*

The more I stood beneath the sky, the more I longed to strip myself of academic jargon and stand in the syllables of haikus instead. I dreamt of writing series and series of them—tight, bare-skinned haikus on white sheets of paper. Eventually, I would become one myself: simple and slender in intention, the sound of a whole note resting on the tongue.

Perhaps this desire for inner clarity sounds strange, but I was not. By day, I inhabited my role as a normal college student—studying too much, but also laughing about boys and going out with friends. My only act of rebellion was to read E.E. Cummings as I walked to campus instead of texting or scrolling through social media. It was a small, unmarked edition that revealed stanzas of astonishing clarity when opened. In the winter chill, the words often dove for my throat, arresting my breath as I stepped over snowbanks, as I climbed hilly stairs.

And sometimes when I was invited to parties, I would say *thank you, but I will be busy that night.* Then I'd go home and try to pound out words from a pen, shaking it and shaking it and peering down its throat:

Hello?

Are you in there, life?

And who will hear you when I'm gone?

But the light is being swept away and I am still sitting in the garden, the notebook open on my lap.

I throw the pack over my shoulders and hurry down the road until I see an ancient fountain equipped with modern plumbing. A carved angel gazes beatifically over the spicket as I fill up my canteens and drink. *Perfect for baths as well*, I think, smiling for my luck.

Just past the fountain, I find a smaller dirt road that leads into the woods. The entrance is barred half-heartedly with a chain hanging from low poles on opposite sides.

This is it, I think. *The path that leads home.*

Beside the chained barrier is a post with a green sign, naming the trail and where it leads. I pull out my camera and snap a photo of it, thinking *evidence*. If someone finds my camera, they'll find where I came from. And that means something.

I close my camera and begin to hike. I hike for an hour at least, but nowhere do I find the place I'd imagined: a small clearing nestled in a protective ring of trees—secluded, yet accessible, somewhere overlooked and undiscovered by other human beings.

I pass an encased statue of the Virgin Mary, followed by a small church surrounded by fire-blackened trees, their branches now lying as inches of ash beneath. The forest floor is littered with animal bones. I nudge a pelvis with my boot, shattering a constellation of rays that clung like a skittish animal to the bone.

A nun emerges from the door of the chapel, moves her head to glance at me, and then spins around and walks deliberately back inside.

Well, I think, remembering the nun in Florence who denied me a place to sleep. I shake my boots of ash and get back on the road. I walk until I find a small village where old men stare at me foggily while they walk their horses down newly paved roads.

Finally, I walk back. I want to be closer to the city, I decide, even if it is not as secluded as I would like it to be.

And that is how I settle on this small clearing by the power line. It isn't unfrequented by humans (I find beer cans and a petrified sock in the grass), but it is shrouded by thick thorn bushes that may dissuade hikers, and it's close to the city. If anything happens, I can run for help.

The grass is worn flat between some clumps of bushes, the perfect size for a sleeping body. About twelve feet from the sleeping spot is an oak tree, covered with thorny vines that tangle the branches of the nearby bushes.

Here I will dig a hole for storage, I think, crouching down to feel the ground against my palm. But the sky is becoming melancholy with its last rays, the soil nearly smothered with dark. So I swing the backpack over my shoulders and begin walking back to the bus station for my survival pack.

The guard smiles at me when I sling it over my shoulders. "Is that a curtain?"

"Uh, yeah," I smile warily. "It's a survival pack."

His smile widens.

I open my mouth to respond but turn around instead. So what if I'm ridiculous? I won't be wearing this pack around town after tonight anyway; it's much too conspicuous.

I walk back outside as the stars begin puncturing the darkness, trying to imagine that red pin in my brain, trying to surrender myself to its urgent meaning again and again.

It is then that I meet the boy with the dog.

How does a writer emphasize significance in a story? Upon which details should the narrative gaze linger?

I had already circled the cathedral three or four times, searching ever more frantically for the university. The university had somehow led me into the gardens, which bordered the dirt road which led me to camp.

Already I am lost, I think. *Already I don't belong in this city of labyrinthine cobblestoned streets.* At the top of the cathedral stairs, I lean against the stone wall to relieve my shoulders of the pack's weight.

"*Vine*! Vine!" I hear, so I crane my neck around the corner. From a distance, they are both dark-haired and thin. They are locked in a playful dance around the ancient well, the boy laughing loudly as he tugs on a rope toy from the dog's mouth. I find myself smiling as I watch them. Then I rise to my feet and approach slowly.

"Perdón," I interrupt. "¿Sabes dónde está la universidad?"

He spins around to look at me, and I am stunned by the brightness in his eyes. I smile shyly. "Perdón," I repeat.

His eyes soften, his smile matching mine. "It's close," he says, in English. "Would you like me to take you?"

I blink. "How did you know—"

"I can always spot an American." His eyes are laughing.

I am annoyed. In Italy, everyone mistook me for Italian, in Turkey they insisted I must be Turkish (at least genetically), and here in Spain, most people assume I'm from Argentina, as I speak Spanish with an Argentine accent. The anonymity feels both freeing and safe. How could a stranger see right through me? *Must be the pack*, I comfort myself, as he calls to the dog.

"Follow me." He spins around and begins walking up the street. "Your name?" he asks.

"Sondra."

"And why are you here, Sondra?"

"Here…?"

"In Catalonia, in Girona…what are you doing here?"

"Oh, well, I'm a writer. So I'm here to write."

"About what, may I ask?"

"Excuse me, but your English is practically perfect. How?"

"I'm a musician. I've got to speak English if I'm gonna get big."

"And what sort of musician are you, exactly?"

"Ah, you know, folk music. Passenger, Mumford and Sons, that kind of thing. Just me and the guitar."

"Do you write your own music?"

He turns to me, nodding. "I do. I'm a writer like you."

"Hmm."

"Here it is!" he announces, throwing an arm at a single building. It's bland Medieval gray, and I don't recognize it.

"Uh… is there a dirt road nearby? They said they lived by a dirt road."

"I'm sorry, who exactly are you looking for?"

"I'm teaching English to a family here, and they—"

"Address?"

"No address."

"What do you mean, no—where's your phone? We'll call them."

"No phone. I don't have a phone."

"Huh," he laughs. "No address. No phone." He raises an eyebrow.

"Yup. Just…a dirt road."

He sighs. "Last name?"

"No…they didn't say."

"Are you sure it's safe to work for a family with no last name?"

I shrug, scratching the dog behind its ears.

"Okay. Well, let's go."

I follow him down a narrow alleyway, touching my back pocket for the comforting feel of my pepper spray. We pass the cathedral again, and then a synagogue.

"Don't worry," he says. "I won't leave you until I watch you walk in their door with my own two eyes."

I laugh vaguely, looking at our surroundings to distract me. We are in a new development, houses cut from cold, straight lines and halo-ed with fluorescent street light. They are harsh and clean compared to la parte antigua with its jumble of streets and weather-worn buildings.

The boy stops beside me, pointing. "It's gotta be here. There is a trail over there, and this is the only neighborhood nearby."

The trail isn't mine and I recognize nothing of our surroundings. I bring a hand to my forehead, rubbing my temples. "Listen…I really appreciate this, but I can find it from here. I am sure it's close."

He shakes his head. "I'm not leaving until I know you're safe."

We are standing beneath a florescent streetlamp, his eyes sharp with that indefinable energy.

"Huh," I nod. I fold my arms across my chest. "Okay, well, fine. I—" He steps forward expectantly, so I turn around and speak into the darkness instead. "I'm looking for a spot to sleep in the woods."

"Excuse me?"

I spin around. "I'm *sleeping* in *the woods*."

He throws up his arms. "Why the hell didn't you tell me? You'll stay with me tonight!"

"No, I don't want to stay with anybody. I...do wilderness survival," which is true.

His eyes widen. "Oh. Oh, I see."

"I'm sorry for lying. But I'm a foreign girl and all alone, and I can't just tell every stranger I meet that I'm sleeping in the woods."

He shakes his head. "I do wilderness survival too, you know."

"Really?"

"Cash and I"—nodding to the dog— "we practically live in these woods."

"It sounds like we have some things in common."

He smiles. "I'll show you a good place to sleep. Will you come see me play on the cathedral steps sometime?"

"Yes. Yes, I would love that."

"Then for the last time I'll say, 'follow me.'"

He leads me down the dirt road, up a small hill, and to a big tree.

"Here," he says, "this should be good for tonight until you find your spot in the morning."

I drop my pack by the trunk and the dog presses his nose into my hand. "He likes you," the boy says. "Cash and I would like to see you again. Find me on Facebook."

I nod, writing his name in my notebook. "And I'll look for you at the cathedral. Thank you."

He calls to the dog and I watch them disappear down the path. Then I lay my head against the tree trunk, smiling hard against my will. It's not that I am in love; I am not so desperate as that. But as I untie my pack, pull on all of my clothes and wrap myself in the tarp, I can't deny that an idea is filling up my insides with light.

Maybe this unspeakable instinct was about finding him, I think, *about finding a person who understands me, who can free me from the loneliness that sent me running to the trees—*

It sounds silly, but I met a beautiful musician on my first night, who speaks perfect English, loves wilderness survival, and looked at me like that beneath the lamplight, as if he grasped all my complexity in a single glance. It was too poetically organized, like a moment when all the past and future scurries into new formations just so that this moment could be.

I shake my head. But laying in the dark beneath the tree where he led me, a giddiness balloons up from my bones, humming me to sleep.

I do not sleep.

Not well, at least.

It's my fault. I left my sleeping bag in Florence as a symbol of new-found maturity after renouncing this ridiculous idea of sleeping in the woods. But now I am ridiculous, and also cold.

I wear all of my clothes and wrap myself in the tarp and small curtain. But I awake soaked in dew and my body never dries. I shiver all night, tossing in the dirt.

Finally, gray pinks my eyelids with light and I roll flat on my back, staring up at the sky.

Small birds rustle in an elm tree above. A few flutter off their branches and plunge their wings up and down up and down, catapulting themselves into the wide expanse. The light is becoming white, antiseptic. It colds through my body as I think: *Someday I will be like that bird, my life like a tiny pair of wings being flung into an expansive sea.*

I should stop all this talk of death. I am young. Twenty-four years old.

The cold drives me out of the tarp and out of all my layers. I pull on a single pair of leggings and a white shirt and roll up my belongings, tying them into a pack. Then I tie up my boots and walk down the hill to the dirt road.

The sun conquers slowly, stroking the gray away with light.

When I find my original camp spot, I drop both packs and pull out a garden shovel from the daypack.

Beneath the oak tree, between the ancient roots, I begin digging. By the time the sun has awakened fully, the hole is three feet deep. I hike to a Medieval fortress down the road to gather slabs of worn wood, which I use to reinforce the dirt walls of the hole. I place the survival pack inside, cover it with a slab of wood, a large stone, rocks, dirt, and vines. When I finish, it looks natural, nothing interesting for a passing hiker to investigate.

I take a string of prayer beads from my pack, a gift from a Muslim friend in Turkey. Each bead is blue with a white circle in the middle. "They will protect you from the evil eye," she told me, and I noticed suddenly that they were tiny eyes, appraising me. I don't know exactly what the "evil eye" means, but here in this small clump of bushes the beads mean companionship, mean that somewhere there are people who love me. I hang them on a small branch by the dirt where I will sleep.

Blue emboldens the sky as I look around camp and see my ideas crystallized. I now have a secret camp in a clump of thorny, vine-covered bushes and trees. In Spain, no less. In Girona. It may be nothing but a clump of earth cells, but my chest contracts warmly as I see the covered pit, the tarp on the ground, the prayer beads swaying from the tree branch. In me swells a warmth like the sensation of home.

Home. Now that is a word worth holding. The first sound like an exhale, but the "m" catching it mid-escape, boundarizing the syllable so it can mean a thing. A consonant like a wall. My walls never stayed in place. We moved every year of my childhood and youth, like we were fleeing—poverty, probably. My dad worked hard, but the ten of us always landed short of getting by.

I learned to find comfort in the constant sensation of change. Places were impersonal backdrops for school or work. I made friends easily but remained aloof. I read and wrote and lingered always on the boundaries, watching. From the margins, looking in, I learned people in communities are strange animals. Almost always, they are acting.

I press the pen to a new page.

Solitude is the solution. We must test the integrity of each thought before the open sky.

But the sky is not so easily flattered. As I sit in the dirt and stare upward, my thoughts begin to reorganize. *We must grind our words to dust and let them fertilize the earth.*

I dig my fingers into the dirt, as if probing for thought-remnants. I close my notebook, rise to my feet, and hike back to the city to find the university library.

There, I breathe the air-conditioned cold as I wander the aisles of books, fan the pages, feel the words with my fingers like braille. I sit at a desk and open a massive book of art, full of colored photographs of old paintings. I flip through the pages until my eyes burn dry. Then I sit back and watch the sky fall apart, its light fractured and gushing gold over ancient stones.

The cathedral bell tolls the hour, sonorous and deep. The wind lifts a flag on the building across the street, under a window that appears to be asleep.

Tomorrow and tomorrow and tomorrow, I think, Shakespeare ringing in my brain as I head back to camp to sleep.

My boyfriend did not approve of Spain.

His name is David, and he is everywhere. His cologne rises up from a stranger's collar, his face looms imminent before every corner, his arms are holding me now as I struggle to sleep—

He doesn't write me anymore.

He said he would no longer play victim to the fragility of my love, how I string him along deeper and deeper and then suddenly look at him like a stranger and say I just need "time."

"Again and again," he said (and here I always sighed).

"What you don't know is that we are soulmates and all the time in the world can't change the way we jibe," he said.

So, you see? I think.

He loves me, even if he no longer writes.

I awake wondering about the strangeness of love, my notebook cracked open in hopes of illumination.

I'm not thinking of the excitement of a new connection, like the one shared with the boy a few nights past. I'm thinking about the trace that lingers after a connection of immense proportions. This trace is not even so tangible as a memory. It's a color, like the blue of David's eyes. It's the circle of cold that a warm mug leaves behind. I think it is the voice that has trailed me through the streets of Italy, Turkey, and Spain: a presence like an absence, a bullet left in the body.

And I knew I was done for the first moment David approached me. I was sitting on a bench when I saw his leather loafers and looked up from my book.

"You're in my Arabic class," I said.

His eyes smiled through a pair of unfashionable glasses. "What are you reading?"

Something about the Middle East, supplementary reading for my minor. We talked about politics and traveling, and being with him was strange, as if we had talked on this bench a thousand times before. I tried to shake him throughout the day. But the next afternoon I sat on that same bench at the same time, reading.

"Hi again," he said, and I feigned surprise.

"Oh hello," I made room for him on the bench. "How are you?"

His face teased with that confident smile. "I don't have much time, but can I have your number?"

"Um, sure. Maybe we can hang out sometime." I typed my number into his phone, too nervous to say the word "date."

He held my gaze, his face thoughtful. "I'll see you soon," he said.

And he left me on that little bench. *Our* little bench, as we'd come to call it.

He picked me up that Friday and we went to Barnes and Noble's, where we drank hot chocolate and wandered the aisles, talking about everything. I kept marveling that we had only just met. We found a globe, put our fingers on it and spun. Where would we travel next? He was going to Russia, I to the depths of the Atlantic Ocean. We laughed.

And then I said, "I am actually going to Spain next summer." I watched him and his eyes stayed open, waiting. So I told him about my plans to live in the woods. I struggled to give a reason. "As a sort of experiment," I ventured.

As we sat at the base of a plastic tree in the children's section, as he listened quietly, I felt that he knew my reasons better than I did. He always knew. He saw straight through my excuses, my flightiness, my pleas for "time."

He saw me from the start, just as if he were born with me, lived with me, and meant to take me to my grave.

How can I run from a love like that?

It chases me through the streets.

I am sleeping very little.

I dug a hole, which helped relieve the discomfort of a hip grinding into the hard dirt, but the cold still gnaws me hungrily each night.

My goal is now to sleep as late and long as possible. Sleep comes easier when the sun is out to heat the leaves and soil beneath me.

While I wait for warmth, I read Plato's *Republic*, which is much drier than philosophy professors claim, and Rousseau's *Confessions*, which is deeply embarrassing. Then I sleep for another hour or so. When my eyes struggle open, I can't possibly sleep longer. My legs itch to explore the streets.

I find a big *mercat*, where I buy a few cans of beans and whole grain bread, and a few days later, a plastic bin of crackers.

Then I walk back at dusk and find the university library, open and beating with the hearts of a billion words arranged in the bodies of books. The books are beautiful in a way that nature is not—the books are crammed with human frailty, and that touches me.

The sun begins laying its rays horizontally over the earth. I find my forest path and walk home, passing a few people walking dogs, some who nod and most who look carefully away.

While they look carefully away, I walk freely, and the sun splatters hotly through the streets.

Back to the library again—beans and bread in the university courtyard, books and writing.

I write about the boy with the dog. I write about David. I wish I could purge all this love from my veins, but it bleeds as liberally as the Spanish sun, painting innocent passersby with its heat.

*I have all kinds of oceans raging inside me.
I have all kinds of skies.*

Then I stop writing and start thinking practically.

I will wash my hair, as it feels greasy when I brush it. There are too many tourists by the angel fountain during the day, so I wait until dusk for privacy, but not until dark, so that my hair has time to dry before I sleep.

I leave the library as the sun starts imploding, streaking entrails of peach and nectarine across the faded sky-sheet. I walk through streets and gardens until I arrive at the vine-covered fountain, drop my bag, and look around. The street and garden are empty.

I turn on the fountain, duck my head beneath it, and run my fingers through my hair, letting the water slide between the strands and soak my scalp with cold. When I turn off the fountain and lift my head, I see an elderly man strolling by and he meets my gaze with a smile.

"Hace calor, eh?" he laughs.

"Sí, mucho calor," I say, and sit down on the stone steps, wringing out my hair until he rounds the corner out of view. Then I pull out the shampoo from my pack and squeeze it into my scalp, lathering quickly and placing my head under the fountain again.

When the water runs clear and I lift my head, no one is watching, and I smile in relief.

I brush my hair quickly, ringing out as much water as I can before I pick up my pack and walk briskly through the city streets, letting the wind blow it dry.

I feel victorious, in spite of myself.

I feel I have accomplished some feat of independence, in spite of myself.
And I think of the boy, in spite of myself.

He had messaged me on Facebook, said he wanted to see me soon.

And when he did, I would greet him with clean, apple-scented hair.

To celebrate, I buy a muffin at a café.

The next day, actually, so maybe it wasn't a direct celebration of washing my hair. Maybe it was a celebration of life, or maybe it was a justification.

I sit at an outdoor table and watch the pigeons bob their heads for crumbs, shuffling their small feet behind them. The muffin is not as good as I expect it to be, and I feel bad for having spent the extra money.

The heat radiates from the cobblestones beneath, magnetizing me into a drowsy half-sleep. I bob my head like the pigeons, fighting dreams, until I finally snap to attention and rise to my feet.

I escape to the air-conditioned library to write. I awaken in the cool indoor air, writing fifty pages of a book that I am still living. How can I weave meaning into a story with an unknown ending? I pull descriptions from my notebook, the action centering around the boy. He will be the mysterious lover, I decide. I brainstorm ways this book could end.

Scenario number one: I stay in Spain. After this month in the woods, I find a real job and then rent a flat. I keep writing books, and the boy keeps writing songs. Soon he realizes that our feelings are a feasible thing, and we enter a love affair rooted in independence and passionate creativity. I barely know the boy, so this is, of course, a fantasy. But perhaps I could stay for the sea, for the Medieval buildings and for Gaudí.

Scenario number two: I fly back to the United States. I enter the cool productivity of a focused college student and stop seeking adventures in far-off places. I choose David. *Was there ever another choice?*

Yes. There are always other choices if we are brave enough to part with the safe and the good.

I shut the laptop, close my eyes, and surrender to thinking. No, *absorbing*. There is another language lurking deep beneath the sentences of this page. It's the language of those who are tuned to the primal beat of things, to the air-conditioned gray of the library, the carpet stifling the gentle wind of students breathing, clearing their throats, crossing and uncrossing their legs, typing.

After a few long breaths, my brain becomes clean as a slip of paper, undulating gently. I see the window and the sun through it. The library is carpeted and the students are meek, engrossed in stale old books that have long since stopped their breathing.

I notice my breath begins to match the boy's in the cubicle next to me, until I shake my head and flick my eyes to the bookshelves, trying to go inward instead.

Is conformity such a plague, anyway? Or is it how we connect?

Perhaps we stand stiff and learn our lessons so that one day we may sing in unison, free *por fin* from all these pesky, misshapen selves.

In the library we are caught up in cool spaces and quiet books. Outside, the sun stalks hotly through the streets.

I had only mentioned Spain that day to remind him.

David already knew, of course, as I had told him on our very first date.

But, he countered, "I thought things had changed." He meant that we had fallen in love.

"Well, they have," I admitted, glancing up from my laptop. We were at the library, studying. "But I can't just abandon my plans."

"I can come with you," he offered, but I shook my head vigorously as I checked a citation, not even bothering to meet his eyes.

This must have angered him, because soon we were arguing in biting whispers. Then he was wiping wetness from his eyes and I was dragging him to some nearby bookshelves so the students would stop glaring.

We sat on the floor between the shelves and held hands. I didn't speak, because I had nothing significant to say.

"I'm sorry," he started. "I just don't know why you'd want to leave me. You know I would never leave you."

I stared at our hands, the way his tented mine as if to protect. Then I glanced at the bookshelves and scanned the titles quickly, feeling my right foot begin tapping beneath my folded legs.

"I..." I began, to buy time. *London's Lost Rivers*, I read, and *The Complete Language of Flowers*. "I'm not leaving you, like you said. I am leaving, but not *you*." I didn't know what I was saying.

"Sondra, I just…don't know what you're looking for. I want you to be happy. But you'll leave in the spring and come back in the fall and you'll be the same woman and we'll be just as in love."

I smiled slightly, in spite of his pain. *As if love were a thing that endures.*

His hands pressed warmly into mine as I thought, *every day I'm a new woman with a new love waiting.*

Well, we are all of us foolish when we're young, I comforted myself in Italy.

I would go home and marry him—*yes maybe even marry him!*—and we'd settle down and buy a house and perhaps birth a few blue-eyed lovelies, compact and sharp-witted like David. The images flickered dimly, persistently through my pack-supported head on a park bench. I was in an ugly suburb of Florence, and the scene was everything you wouldn't expect from an exotic trip to Italy: muggy, mediocre scenery. The patchy grass of a neglected park beside a dingy gas station where I used the bathroom and didn't buy anything. My stomach howled with hunger while my camera sat buried in my pack, superfluous here.

And I thought: *I am tired of this.*

I had started the summer in Rome, working on a sailboat moored in the Tiber River in exchange for room and board. The boat owner was a foul-mouthed Scot enamored with Rome's good, cheap wine. Then there was the young Spaniard who arrived before me, a bushy-bearded man whose muscular arms were patterned with tattoos. While I scrubbed at an algae-encrusted lifeboat during the day, the Spaniard worked on a complicated project in the engine room, emerging in a shroud of white dust when he needed air or a glass of water. I trailed him through the boat with a broom, cleaning up after him.

The Tiber River is darkly polluted, and one of our chores was to keep the trash moving through its veins. We wielded long-hooked metal poles to nudge the wading microwaves, shoes, bottles, and chairs down their way, pushing the problem to another boat. And I thought, *a river is like a transparent earth*. Stocked with the relics of centuries, we watch objects from people dead or alive decompose before our eyes.

It was a little sickening living directly above this waste, on a boat which rocked gently in its filth while we slept. One night I dreamt that I fell into the river while moving the trash methodically with my metal hook, the waters filling my lungs with its phlegmy pus.

And then Paul joined us, a middle-aged Northern Irishman with an accent so strong that I waited seconds before responding to anything he said, just to be sure I had translated the phrase properly in my head. He was fatherly and kind to me, even though we disagreed on almost everything. He came with me that Friday to the city and wrote me a sonnet outside an overpriced pizzeria by the colosseum.

I only stayed in Rome for a week, but the work-exchange saved me precious money. Then I went to Florence with no such arrangement, having to pay for a hostel and realizing that I was missing 100 euros. I had planned to survive in Europe on the small direct deposit I received every few weeks for researching and writing a Western philosophy textbook with a professor. But with the missing money, I had only twenty-five euros left, exactly enough for one night at the cheapest hostel in town. *One night*, and my professor wouldn't pay me for a few more days.

I was careless for misplacing my money, but now I was stranded. My parents rarely had twenty dollars in their bank account, so I didn't consider asking them for help. As a middle child of eight, I had long ago stopped asking for favors.

I walked all morning to the highest part of Florence, where I knocked on a convent door, hoping these were nuns who take a vow of hospitality. The blue-eyed abbess was exceedingly gracious at first. "I lost my money in Rome," I explained, and her smile didn't budge as she said, "I believe you."

"I have twenty-five euros," I offered.

"Our rooms are fifty."

"Yes, I know, but I don't have fifty."

"Our rooms are fifty."

"What do you pro—"

"I suppose you will have to sleep on the streets." Her smile was unmoving.

"Oh, yes. I am so sorry to come here…" I grabbed my backpack and pushed my sunglasses to my face so she wouldn't see the tears welling in my eyes. Humiliation followed me as I walked for hours away from the city, searching for a place to sleep. There was nowhere secluded, and I refused to sleep on the streets.

So I walked until I was too weary to keep walking and laid on this park bench to rest. It was not a good place for the night, but perhaps a nap of an hour or two. I felt the humidity seep into my body, sogging my brain like wet bread. *David, David, David.* His name echoed like a mantra, a rough translation of the presence I felt swelling around me. *David, David.* Without him, I am exiled as a stranger to the streets. Without him, I am laying on a muggy park bench in these ugly surroundings. Without him—

I sat up, a resolution seizing me. *I have learned my lesson*, I thought. In my mind there was another bench where David and I had met, and it seemed to grow closer as I walked to the hostel.

I can't live without him, I can't live without him, my brain recited. This whole trip was childish! Did it mean anything but a flight from love? David was perfect for me—this could not be doubted. And yet I had doubted; I was wracked with doubt. "This will be a good opportunity," I had told him, "to figure out what we want."

But as I walked for hours—back to the city, back to the hostel where I handed the receptionist the last of my money—the blue of David's eyes laughed through my very own lids like the subtle pulsation of sky. He was right, maybe, about love being a sensation which stays. There would be no more sleeping outside. I would find a way to get money for the next few nights in Italy. Then I would fly home.

The next morning, a small miracle. Paul messaged me on Facebook: "Found your money in the pillowcase. Will be coming to Florence today and I'll bring it with me." We spent the afternoon together and then I took a bus to Venice, leaving my sleeping bag draped over the balcony of the hostel. After a few days it would be picked up, I assumed, by someone who would actually use it.

I came to my senses in Venice. Did I think David would be back on that bench of our first beginning, waiting for me? I had left him. There could be no going home until I figured out why. After all, I had planned to come here before I'd even met David. He may right about me running, but it's not from him.

In an alleyway by a Venetian canal, I began to write, revising my story with my decision to stay.

I suppose we are all like that nun. Not brave enough to be good, we succumb to our own bureaucracy of being, doing what is acceptable simply because it is being done and has before been done.

So I must be brave. I must go to the woods in Spain. Because—

Brave-less bureaucracy ties the soul in red-taped death.

I was doing it again—pontificating. Writing true words, but in the improper place.

Maybe Spain is about that. Recognizing falsity.

But as I read the last line, I was suddenly angry, wanting to erase everything. Anything I write about this senseless performance art piece feels like a desecration.

The truth is that I am trying to dislodge a bullet from my body.

Maybe there is a clue engraved on it, or maybe it is blank. Only the pain is real. Only the need.

I walked back to my Airbnb in Padua while clenching and unclenching a fist. Meanwhile, the blue of David's eyes seemed plastered all over the skies, lurking beneath peeling terracotta walls and glinting off glass surfaces.

For two days, I ate a jar of Nutella while I wandered the Venetian canals in a state of sugared giddiness and artificial energy. On the third day I was paid, and crossed the street to a market to buy a thin package of spaghetti noodles, tomato sauce, and a jar of olives. I cooked in the kitchen of the Airbnb and went to the bedroom to eat (wood-floored, a few rays of sun on the floor), popping olives in my mouth between bites of sauce-drenched spaghetti.

Someday, I thought—David's face rising always before me—*Someday I will be good enough to love him.*

The next day I took a flight from Milan to Istanbul, where I stayed for six weeks with an elderly woman, for a small price. From Istanbul to Vidreres, where I taught English to the girls in the sun-flickering house near the beach.

And then Girona. Because the sky was still stalking me.

At dusk, I walk back to camp and sleep.

Try to, at least.

In the morning, I sleep more.

I go to a café and find the boy with the dog has messaged me, inviting me to dinner. My hair is still okay, though maybe not so appley.

I say yes.

Of course, I am thrilled. My writing seems sonnet-like and I barely think of David all day.

Is it so easy to replace true love? *What is true, anyway?*

My guilt gets lost in philosophy and I wear lipstick, just in case.

He smiles when he opens the door.

"Hi," I say, smiling back.

"It's good to see you." And then, "Down!" to the dog, pulling him by the collar as he charges me.

"No, no," I say, stooping down to pet him. "I had a fantasy of finding a stray dog when I got here and feeding it so it would keep me company."

The boy crouches down too. "There aren't many strays here."

"I noticed. So when I saw you and the dog, I think I was drawn to—"

How could I end that sentence? *To you? To the dog?* I can only think that his breath feels uncomfortably warm as he raises his eyes.

"—your relationship," I say. "I can see he means a lot to you."

The boy simply holds my gaze, a smile pulling at the corner of his lips. Then he pats the dog on the head and stands up, moving to the kitchen.

"I looked up your writing," he says, turning on the light and taking out a pan. "Sorry. Dinner isn't finished."

My throat tightens. "How did you find my writing?"

"Just Googled your name. I found a blog."

"A blog?" I gasp, and I feel naked, as I always feel when someone reads my writing without permission. "Last I had a blog was…maybe six years ago."

"Maybe," he laughs, filling the pan with water and turning on the stove.

"Oh, it was awful, wasn't it?" I ask, hopelessly.

"No, just…angsty. There were only two posts."

I nod, touching my throat. "Yeah."

"It's messy," he states, throwing a glance across his kitchen.

"I don't mind," I lie, craving the cleanliness of camp.

He rolls a peeled onion onto a cutting board, dicing with a smoothly rocking knife. The air sharpens with acidity.

"How is it?" he asks, as he pours oil into a pan. "Under the tree?"

"It's good. It's hard, but it's good," and I think triumphantly of washing my hair.

"Well, you just let me know if you ever need anything. I can help." He wipes his hands on a dish towel and rummages through a cabinet before pulling out two cans of tuna. "It's not much…" he falters, and hands them to me.

"Thank you," I say, disappointed because I don't like tuna and I would have to eat them now out of gratitude, out of frugality.

I place the cans in my backpack. "Can I help?" I ask, but he shakes his head as he leans over the stove. "Cooking is art," he explains, now sliding the onions into the oil with a sizzle. "It relaxes me."

I go to the living room to sit on the couch, the dog trailing behind. Darkness has swept away the last rays of sun, and night bears upon this room like a tide. I make myself aware, trying to divine clues into the boy's inner life.

The smell of weed, for one. An apartment long steeped in old breath and sweet smoke. I glance at the coffee table to see two half-smoked joints. *Two*. Is that significant?

There are two bookshelves (not significant), on either side of an arched entryway to another room. The book titles are blurred by distance from the couch (fiction? non-fiction? poetry?) but at least I know he reads.

I crane my neck to see the room beyond the bookshelves, but the lights are off. All I can see is a guitar leaning against the wall, remnants of blue dusk spilling from an open window onto its wooden body. The blue light and dark shadows flicker and wrestle, the blue resisting the flood.

Resisting the *night*, I mean. Resisting the chaos that creeps into our day-boats and begins blurring boundaries. Like this feeling settling over my skin that this dark-eyed boy can deliver me from the cold brutality of the sky, from the ever-vastening night that threatens to cleanse the ground beneath me. *The darkness has many eyes*, I think, surveying the shadows sliding over the coffee table, glistening over the dog's slick fur, *and they blink over the room like an animal bristling with life.*

"It's ready," says the boy, and I look up to see his satisfied smile, a white plate in each hand.

"It smells amazing," I say, taking my chair.

"Pasta with sauteed mushrooms and onions, pancetta, and...." he pauses, "Oh yes, and a drizzle of truffle oil."

When he meets my eyes, I feel compelled to glance away. I want to linger in his gaze, but I sense that something is wrong. Staring down at my pasta, I suddenly know. The brightness in his eyes (equal parts guilt and attraction), the two joints on the coffee table. They are subtle clues, but I feel almost certain of the conclusion: *He has a girlfriend.*

"Maybe I know why you came here," he says, after swallowing.

I look up from my plate.

"You need your freedom," he states.

I smile slightly. "Don't we all?"

"That's right," he nods, glancing vaguely at the couch. "We all do."

I apply myself to the plate, devouring the noodles. After a few days of only beans and bread, this pasta redefines "delicious." It's all I can do to maintain a semblance of politeness as I eat.

Besides, there is only so much of the boy's gaze that I can bear. I have decided we are incompatible, but every glance into his eyes weakens the conclusion. I remind myself of the facts: he must be younger than me, and seems to have no plans for higher education. And maybe I am wild now, but this isn't really my style. Back home I lived by a heavily marked planner, earning good grades and planning for graduate school. Maybe I didn't know or care much about finances, but I still lived frugally and fit well into society.

The chemistry is undeniable (its pulls us closer as we converse), but chemistry doesn't pay the bills. It gives no guarantees and offers no longevity. *Don't ask me about David*, I think. David is not a musician or a writer; he doesn't burn through life like a bullet. Good thing, too! Otherwise, we'd be nothing but two singed holes in the fabric of life. David holds me together. He grounds me without compromising my identity.

But I left David, I remind myself. I left David and here is the boy, watching me with that dark attention that opens my body to its heat.

He bends over the table now and then, so close that I can feel his breath. He says things like, "What did you do back home?" and I want to laugh at him. Because what I did was wait for freedom.

No. That's not right—What I did was study, *and study happily*, I remind myself.

I was not waiting for Spain, was not waiting to be swept into the world of this stranger who leans over the table, smiling with increasing openness, the guilt softening.

I was happy, and I was alone.

No, not alone. *I was with David.*

My thoughts slip. The heat of his closeness absorbs directly through my skin. *This is the risk of the night*, I think. When language fractures and we are thrown into the waters of the original deep. I feel attached to myself by ever-thinning strings of circumstance, ever-fraying adjectives of self-identification. What is age or compatibility? *Accidental.* Our mutual understanding? *Fundamental.*

The flood of darkness. The brightening eyes. The sharp-edged fantasy of awakening beneath the same weak-edged sun.

"Do you know why it feels like death?" he asks, with a sudden ironic smile.

He means Girona, I assume. I had told him that it's haunting me, making me think of my mortality.

"The age, I guess."

"Not according to some traveling Kabbalistic Jews. I met one here about a year ago. She gave me an occult tour of the city, told me that it's built on underground canals."

I imagine ancient waterways flowing beneath the cobblestone, silt-rich and darkly polluted.

"And why is that death?" I ask, my lips teasing into a smile.

He looks beyond me, to the bookshelf maybe, or the guitar that leans against the wall in the other room.

"Something that runs beneath?" he suggests, "doesn't that feel like death to you?"

"How poetic," I say, and we laugh, the tension loosening.

I could kiss him, I think. Could ride that tension to its release.

But the night never lasts, and we are always and forever chained to the waking world. We cannot remain in naked understanding. We must dress ourselves each morning in our names, nationalities, and beliefs. We don our relationships like second skins. We step into memory and regret.

You can run to the woods, but society always wins. It wins each time you think a thought. It wins when it wakes you from your dreams.

He lets me out the door, and I exhale into the streets, trying to shake the feeling that the heat of his breath is stalking me.

I am in love, I think, when I awake in the morning.

A ridiculous idea, but as concrete as the air I breathe.

Could he love me too? Could he love me too? The question rises with me, emptying my exhaustion, an urgent reminder of that red pin in my brain.

The sky sent me here to find, to find—

The boy?

Perhaps every act of authenticity draws like-minded loves into your orbit.

And isn't that enough?

As I walk the streets, his dark gaze lands with a thud again and again in my gut.

I saw it a few days ago, on my way home from the bus station:

"TWO SLICES FOR ONE EURO." The sign was stamped over a photograph of pizza.

I didn't stop because I had a can of beans in my bag, but today I search for it, hungry and down to a euro and a few cents. I find myself in the immigrant part of town. I see a woman leaning against the wall of a tiny mercat, sucking on a cigarette between her teeth, staring into the empty street.

"Buen día," I approach, and ask her if she has seen a pizzeria nearby.

She pulls out the cigarette but doesn't answer, asking instead, "You're not Spanish?"

"No, American."

"You're not American."

"I am American."

She eyes me suspiciously.

"I learned Spanish in Argentina."

"Yes," she nods, accepting. "You are Argentine. You have that look."

"Yes," I agree, "and the pizzeria?"

"There is a Domino's..." She indicates vaguely down the street.

"No, it wasn't a Domino's. It was another one—a local one, I think."

"Nothing like that," she sighs, suddenly staring at something nondescript in the distance.

"Well, thank you," I say, nodding towards her, though she is already ignoring me. "Thanks again."

She glances at me abruptly as I turn to walk away.

I walk for another hour, but I find nothing. Maybe the deal was a mirage, a dream born of hunger. Maybe I am just awful with directions.

I go to a café instead, use the Wi-Fi to check Facebook as I pick apart a muffin on my plate. A message from my best friend, complaining about how she has to wake up early for work, my other friend telling me she met a guy. Nothing from the boy with the dog.

I place my hand on top of my laptop, closing it slowly as I watch people pass. My plate is covered in the crumbs of lemon poppyseed. I eat them, one by one, while I watch the painting of the Labrador retriever on the wall. Light deepens itself as it loses itself, becoming condensed in the painting of the dog, in the faces of the passersby.

Light.

It is dark now, and I am still sitting in the café. Two poppyseeds left on the plate. I leave them, an offering to something, perhaps, or someone—some god of sun or rain.

Let there be sun, not rain.

A waitress wipes a table nearby. Stops and looks at me expectantly, towel in hand. I stand up, push the plate towards her, walk out the door. It was like this in Italy too. Always wearing out my welcome, always heading back to Mother Nature who is not yet brave enough to expel me.

Camp is waiting for me same as usual, hushed in the dark, rustling with breeze, clothes draping the bushes with a blush of unnatural color. Prayer beads sway slightly, the painted eyes beginning to chip with the cycles of sun and morning dew.

The clouds above are dispersing, surrendering to the clarity of stars. There would be no rain tonight.

I shroud my body in the tarp and let sleep come slowly, jumpily through the cold.

Two days later, the boy invites me to his apartment.

I am forced to swallow a euphoric smile as I hurry back to camp to contemplate. *I can't wear my dress, can I?* I consider its magenta fabric against the grass. He knows I live in the woods.

I pull on my leggings instead, a black shirt. I hurry back to the city and press the intercom to his apartment. "It's me," I say, and moments later, he is opening the building's old door.

He is breathless from having run down the stairs, but his smile seems reserved. "Hi," he states, and I slide by him, climbing the steps to his door.

He's come to his senses, I think. He knows there can be nothing between us. *And the girlfriend*, I remind myself. *There has to be a girlfriend.*

"Do I get a private concert?" I ask.

"Yeah," he laughs. "Yeah, I wanted to play some songs for you."

We are at his door, and he opens it for me. He lets me pass as the dog charges me.

"He's still young," he apologizes.

"I know," I say, scratching his ears.

He leads me to the room between the bookcases. It's mid-afternoon, I realize (did I walk here in a daze?) and it's hot. He pulls a chair from the dining table, placing it before the window in a slice of sun.

"Sit," he beckons, and he goes for a well-worn wooden chair on the other side of the room, placing it a few feet in front of me. The lights aren't on, so the room is dim as he takes his seat, pulling the guitar onto his lap.

I say nothing, waiting.

"Um," he begins, looking down at the strings. "Maybe some Mumford and Sons to begin with?"

"Yeah," I nod.

He pauses another moment, intent on the placement of his fingers. When he begins, I am surprised how effortlessly his voice wraps around the words. I close my eyes, feeling the heat on my face from the window, breathing the un-aired room with its packed repository of smells.

Thoughts invade my brain like characters in a dream. What role will he play in my story? I feel my lips curve into the wisp of a smile. My story is a trap (so is his). How can anyone enter another's life without being distorted, swallowed by their theme? We are always paring away the complexity of the human being, leaving only what relates directly to our narrow personal stories. The violence of the self. Of the author. Of belief.

Thoughts exhaust eventually, leaving only music and lyrics, waves and particles, the white hot center of song between. A sudden silence and my eyes flutter open in surprise.

"Wow," I say, emerging from the song and the heat. His eyes are waiting. "You are very good," I say. "Very good." And I mean it, although I don't know what else to say.

His lip lifts into a smile before strumming the guitar again. Then he stops, clapping his hand over the strings.

"Does your religion make you happy?" he asks, scrunching up his nose.

Oh, I think. Maybe he thinks this is an obstacle: difference in belief.

"You think I'm happy?"

"I *know* you're happy," He's staring at the guitar strings.

I don't know what to tell him, so I say, "Maybe I came here because I was too happy, or too...something."

He laughs, finally raising his eyes to mine. "You're telling me you ran away because you were too happy?"

I don't tell him what I see: a dark-eyed girl locked in a bedroom, screaming through walls. I press my fingers into my forehead, dizzy from the sun that bludgeons against the window. "I was—" I begin, but the girl is kicking against the door now, the Arizona heat pulsing blankly through my brain. "Well." And I fight the images back into obscurity, looking at him directly. "I am too big for a house. I craved the sky."

He pulls back, shrinking from the strength of my gaze. We aren't supposed to speak like this in polite society. But The Scream behind my eyelids demands something of me.

The boy shifts in his chair, gently stroking the guitar strings. Then his eyes rise to meet mine.

"I wish I were as brave as you," he says.

I shake my head. It's not bravery behind me, but necessity.

He leans the guitar against the wall and goes to the living room, stoops over the coffee table. I follow, watching him pick up a joint and light. *One joint* in the ashtray, this time.

"And yes," I add, "my religion makes me happy, I guess."

He collapses on the couch, exhaling smoke as he says, "I don't believe in God." He is smiling, but his voice is tinged with condescension.

"I know," I say, smiling weakly.

I want to say, "neither do I," but he wouldn't understand because he can't see what I am seeing. The little girl again, her jaw clenched in The Scream that pulses even now behind my eyelids: the expansive sensation of heat, a rage as wide as the sky.

I want to tell him that I learned to write when I was barely old enough to read, because the pain took me straight out of my body, both evading and yet demanding speech.

I want to show him where it dropped me: the wasteland where words pant dry, where meanings wander hollowed of their sound-bodies, where new-born and unnamed realities mouth hungrily towards the sun, waiting to be seen into meaning.

God lies here too, long since buried beneath the weight of rationality. But Being still breathes beneath the mounds of debris, a silence that sometimes sounds like speech. I can't ignore these weighty exhalations, so I always claim to believe.

I move to the couch, sitting on the opposite end to leave a buffer for the dog.

"And the wilderness?" he asks, his eyes softened as he leans towards me. "You look good."

"Oh no," I say. "I mean, I don't sleep much without a sleeping bag."

He taps the end of the joint into the ashtray and heads down the hall, opening a door to what I assume is his bedroom. I look at the dog, confused. Then he emerges, cradling a black bag in his arms. He extends it to me, but I don't move.

"Just give it back to me before you leave Spain," he says.

"Are you...sure?"

He nods.

I take it from him, holding it against my chest. "A sleeping bag," I say, my heart pounding.

"Yeah, just take care of it," he shrugs.

The boy doesn't sit down, so I pick up my bag. "I'll leave you," I comply. "You can sing your original songs next time."

"I'll walk you down." I follow him to the door, where I hesitate for a moment. I throw my arms around his neck, and he wraps his arms around my waist and draws me closer. *I know next to nothing about him*, I think. He inhales near my cheek. Exhales through my hair.

"Thank you," I say, pulling away.

He is fighting a smile. *It's like swallowing a whale and trying to keep it inside,* I think, looking at the sleeping bag under my arm as I walk back to camp, thinking *maybe the sleeping bag means something.*

And so a sleeping bag is restored to me, and I sleep soundly for the first time in a week.

Life isn't perfect with the sleeping bag. Somehow I am still cold, but the cold is bearable and the weariness in my face has begun to soften just a bit.

I walk home from the library the next evening just as the rains begin tightening in the sky, preparing for release. And I think, *I suppose I was right to come here.* Because it seems that the world has sprung up to help me, as if it were waiting all along for me to act on just *one true thing*.

This string of words feels italicized in my brain, feels maybe even bolded.

One. True. Thing.

The rains will come soon, I think. But for tonight, just woolen clouds and a gentle drizzle, my head nuzzled deep into the sleeping bag.

The world wakes up shivering with light.

The leaves shiver.

The trees shiver.

I feel the light too; it rattles through my body as if my flesh were transparent. I roll up the sleeping bag and ready for another day. My backpack slides over my shoulders and my headphones over my ears as Beethoven's 5th begins its manic prelude.

I meant what I said to the boy—about being too big for society. It feels something like "spilling over" but I will call it joy, for short. This joy came sudden as a sickness while I studied some mundane subject in the library, while I walked home from school in the evening, while I ate oatmeal in the dimly lit kitchen that I shared with three other students. It seemed no ordinary action was immune from this onslaught of extraordinary life.

Society is not built for those who spill over. It is built for those who rejoice in contained monotony, or in other words, do not rejoice at all.

Now I am in town, drinking spearmint tea at a sun-dappled table. There are pots of orange geraniums on the sills outside. And through me rings the knowing that this moment is an exceptional thing.

Perhaps this joy *isn't quite normal*, but it's a happy side effect of dark origins. Pain is always the origin of the ecstatic, that first spilling out of the body. We spill out of our mothers—bloodly, screaming, and then forever after are trying to keep ourselves un-spilled, untainted by great and breaking pain (and thus love, and thus joy).

Make it concrete, Sondra.

I am rolling my lip between my teeth. I am scraping a nail down my thumb.

What I'm trying to say is: *the pain taught me joy*. But the past tense feels naïve. The past tense ignores that little girl that haunts behind my eyelids, the imprint of her cold and quaking sobs, her hot and angry screams.

The laptop is open. The cursor blinks accusingly, petitioning details.

I will give you a name: childhood depression. Names are meant to smallify a thing to the sayable, to the digestible. But I was diagnosed only once, tentatively, by a therapist whom my parents couldn't afford to pay after the diagnosis. They couldn't afford medication, either so the name slipped into "pain" into "sensitivity" into "something wrong with that child," into the ever-shifting scream with no silencing.

My table is beside the window; the sun strikes my hands and face. I flip my wrist to see the blue veins pulsing and think, *maybe it's an issue of blood*. There were whispers of aunts and uncles with "problems," though I had never met them (our extended family was vast), and the details were hazy. If there were genetic origins, they wouldn't bring me closer to understanding—my family suffocates discomfort with silence, so those conversations wouldn't be possible.

Regardless of origins, "depression" seemed wrong. There was none of that apathy or lack of life in me. No, I was stretched, was pulped, was left out to dry, was—*locked in a bedroom after school*. They didn't know what to do with me, so there I stayed, rolling around the floor, weeping hysterically for hours. You'd think I'd scream myself dry, but the well never emptied. I screamed for years as I felt my brain unraveling, as I thought: this is where sanity ends, *this* there is no surviving.

I am tapping my fingers on the table. I am not breathing.

Breathe.

When I was older, I started to run, hoping to escape. I ran through Arizona's suburbia in the cool nights, alert for coiled rattlesnakes on the street. I ran to the end of the cornfields in Indiana, panting and wet from humidity. I ran through the tidy neighborhoods of mountain-flanked Utah.

SONDRA

And then I ran to Spain.

No. I shake my head. That's not the story. I ran for less personal reasons. But where does one reason end and the other begin? *Can a single thread of life be understood in isolation?*

I sit back from the keyboard, skimming my eyes over the page and feeling the breath clench in my chest. *I should delete this*, I think. People are always blaming those they don't know, as if they understood what it is to be a parent crushed by poverty who thought they would break if they heard a word about their child's pain.

My face is hardening, my fist clenching.

But someone had to break. A parent can break with empathy (and then *do something*), or the child can break again and again and again and again and and again and again and again and again and again and again and again and again and again and again and again

for pages
for years
for lifetimes

So, the words will stay on the page. Because I cannot rip them from my chest—they lay ink-deep as tattoos. They get caught in my throat until I gasp for air, until I choke. And then The Scream swells swells swells through the bones of my body, threatening to fracture the ground of speech. Thoughts fall apart. My body recedes like a boat, sinking. If I write this pain for long enough, I can write myself straight out of speech, into the cold spaceless that brackets the body.

If I stayed there long enough, I'd have to present you with a book splayed of letters in unnatural shapes. I would become an artist of frightening abstraction. I would dismember the world of meaning the way the world dismembered me.

I squeeze my leg with a hand, trying to control its shaking.

Abstraction again. If you want explanations or concrete memories, I will refuse my role as reliable narrator. The memories mean nothing—it's The Scream which structures everything! The pain is not an object, not an event woven into a story. It's the container itself, the ink. It's the wound from which the words worm forth—

SONDRA

Breathe.

I rub my forehead until my thoughts re-order.

When I moved away from home at eighteen, I began improving rapidly. The world simply grayed, deadened. I waded through the sluggish numb for a few years, a small price to pay. Then—

the joy.

It must have been here all along! But The Scream had kept me from its waters. Yes, the pain was too much for me—it pounded out my brain until it spilled into the world. But so did the joy. This is the beauty of staying alive. Not so much the comfort, but the color.

Sometimes the color still stings: flashbacks. When they strike, my body reacts. My middle finger digs into the flesh of my thumb or all five fingers press into my forehead. *No one is coming. You will breathe your last breath behind this door, pounding.*

Pain of a certain pitch cries out for new language. But I have nothing to offer but this body, which wanders nations yelling *see? see!*

I shut my laptop and massage my hand, watching a young couple enter the café beneath the sound of a bell.

Ah, I remember suddenly. Makono took me here. We sat at that table by the window.

My first day in Girona already feels like a blur (besides the fortuitous meeting with the boy), but I remember I never responded to Makono's last Facebook message.

"I will visit my cousin on Sunday," he had written two days ago. "Lunch?"

I am still not sure what to think of him, but he had apologized for hitting on me, and the boy with the dog has messaged me nothing since giving me the sleeping bag, a two-day silence that is beginning to unsettle me.

I open my laptop and respond, "Yeah, tomorrow sounds good. I'll come get you at the bus station."

I lean against the chair and wait for Makono to respond (he is online), while the young man snatches the girl's hat. She spins around in exaggerated horror, scolding him in French. He places the hat back on her tousled blond head and kisses her slowly, pulling her body with his hand on the arch of her back. *Do they think they're in a movie?* I pull my gaze away, annoyed.

"Yes," he writes. "9:30."

"K," I send.

Then I sit back and hug my arms against my ribs, as if to keep them inside.

I will wander forever at this rate, I think, as I walk through the streets, hunting for cheap bread.

Too much writing about the past. It's a relief to have hunger to attend to, and it doesn't take long before I find a small market just a few minutes away from the cathedral. It's surprisingly cheap for this part of town, and the Pakistani owner speaks to me in Spanish, and then English when I tell him my nationality, and then claims he speaks four more languages in addition.

He rings up my bread and a can of beans. Then I see a something familiar: two corn cookies stuffed with dulce de leche and rolled in shredded coconut.

"I thought only Argentines made these," I say, waving the alfajor at him before setting it on the counter.

"Nope," he says, reciting my total. "It started with the Arabs."

I thank him and put the beans in my daypack, holding the alfajor in my hands. Two hands, like a treasure. I take it to one of those narrow cobblestoned streets, sit on a stair beneath the cast iron lamps and hanging geraniums, and eat.

The cookie crumbles in my mouth, caramel oozing through the cracks. Argentina rises up through a haze of memories and I almost remember how people there loved me, how easy it was to be loved. Could it be so easy to be loved?

I sit for a moment, eyes resting on the cobblestones. Then I brush the crumbs from my lap and walk back to camp.

There I lay on the sleeping bag, which comforts me.

I am not so alone, I think, looking at the prayer beads swaying gently on the tree, feeling the sleeping bag fabric against my face. There are people who care about me.

I know the boy was just being kind (not romantic), but I can't help wondering if it means something, a token of *what could be.*

I still know so little about the boy. The easy understanding and yet the fact he is inscrutable means he stays with me as an unsolved riddle. I am trapped in wondering who he is and why he is so recognizable to me, what he means. Besides, the irrational wanting.

"He doesn't like me," I whisper emphatically, shaking my head, watching the dusk shake through the thorny bushes around me.

But he looked up my writing, didn't he? He invited me over for dinner, didn't he? And he didn't mention the fact that he has a girlfriend, although I am almost certain that he does (which is why I won't make the first move—*ethics* and all that).

In any case, *the boy means something.*

"Buen día," I say, squinting at Makono through the powder shade of early blue.

"Hola," he says, in a blue and white button-up shirt. He looks nice, and I hope he's not trying to impress me.

"Should we—?" I begin, and he nods and follows me out of the bus station.

"Breakfast first," he says, and he leads me across the street, where he orders two sandwiches and watches me eat.

"I already ate," he says, when I offer him a piece.

Last time he bought me food, I was trying to get rid of him. Now I observe him, trying to read his character through his gestures and speech. I can think of only a few words to describe him: calm, blunt, and nurturing. We converse between my bites of food, but mostly he watches me like he, too, is looking for clues.

"Tell me about your parents," I say.

He leans forward, sighing. "They're old," he says. "I send them money so they stay healthy. And"—here he smiles impishly— "I'm the favorite, of course." His love for them is palpable, and I smile too.

"You came here for them?" I ask.

He nods. "They need me. So do my cousins back home."

I feel selfish when he asks, "Why did *you* come here?"

"Just the experience," I reply. "It's good to travel, to get to know the world."

He nods, very slowly. There is something he doesn't believe.

I change the subject. "So where do you work now?"

"A bakery. I work a lot, but I have Sundays off."

He asks me to show him the city, and we head to the ancient Roman fortifications, one of the few sightseeing spots I can easily find. We climb a lookout, and he takes pictures of me observing the city below.

"So, are you going to see your cousin now?"

He looks confused. "Oh, no. He is…busy today. I'll just stay with you."

I smile, happy that I don't have to sit around thinking about the boy with the dog and his secret girlfriend.

"Where should we go now?" I falter, having run out of ideas.

"We'll walk," he says, and we spend the rest of the afternoon meandering through the streets, occasionally perching on benches to talk. Sometimes his broken Spanish forces us to mime, but we laugh our way through gestures and explanations. Then he takes me to eat a late lunch and insists on paying again, in spite of my embarrassed protests.

"*Your family*," I emphasize over the table as he signs the check.

He clicks his tongue. "We are fine."

I appraise him through narrowed eyes.

"Don't look at me like that," he scolds. "I will do what I want to do with *my* money." He presses a finger into his chest.

"Okay, okay," I raise my hands.

"And I'll be back next Sunday," he says, handing the waiter the check. "Same time." Then he looks down, suddenly uncertain, "If you…"

"I'll be free," I interject. "I'm always free, on weekends."

He nods gravely and we leave. He carries my daypack to the bus station, where I leave him with a friendly hug.

As he boards the bus, I smile to myself, thinking: *So men can be friends without wanting me. I just have to set boundaries.*

And I walk back to camp as the dusk begins to settle, feeling lighter and less afraid.

I am in the library, trying to revise my life.

Or rather, I'm revising this book, which is a life in miniature, an attempt to coax healing from the symbol-soaked trees.

I stop, stare at the words. I didn't mean to write "healing," but "meaning." I start doodling, wondering why some words seem to suck from the same root of truth. The roots are tangled. And what is the ground beneath?

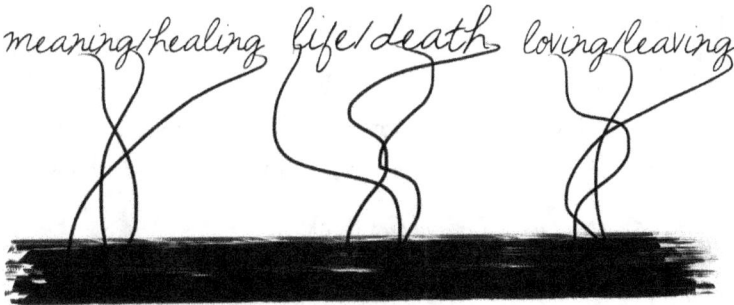

These questions have unseen answers. But the asking slits open possibility. It widens within me, a wordless space like a web of color. I would paint it, but I'm not sure I could land upon the correct shade.

The sun lands on my laptop from the window, and I shift so as not to be blinded.

I review my pages on a Google doc. The boy is a dark scrap of life, infuriatingly beautiful and alive. David is warm, steady, and intelligent, a home I yearn for but may never choose. Makono is a friend, and thus a minor character.

I don't mean to dismiss his friendship, but my current life seems to fall under the "adventure/romance" genre. I am young and men are drawn to me.

I pull a strand of hair before my eyes—it's red to the brink of blood. But the shade is false; I started dying away the faded brown years ago, a rebellion against ashy origins. My eyes are almond-shaped, brown with specks of green in the sunlight, accented by strikingly black brows. So far so good, except my lips aren't thick enough for our selfie era, and my nose is too big.

On the heroine falls the burden of beauty. Women spend lifetimes trying to merit the place of protagonist in their own stories. I have tried to comply with the demands, but when I scrutinize my face and body, I find a thousand failures. I drag a fingernail down, against the inside of my wrist. *I am alive and always leaving*, I remind myself. Men are drawn to that *spilling-over* and drawn more to the promise of temporality.

And I think back to Enzo, who I met on the steps of the San Basilica. I was pretty enough for him, anyway, because he wanted to fuck me.

So we are writing about Enzo now, I think, sighing.

Can a single thread of life be understood in isolation? I wrote the line a few days ago, and it seems to raise an eyebrow at me as I stare at the computer screen.

No, I breathe.

And I begin writing:

I was hungover, by then, on naked statues and tourist-jammed streets. After a week of wandering alone in Florence (I couldn't afford the restaurants or museums), Enzo messaged me on Couchsurfing, offering to teach me Italian and show me the city for free. He had good reviews and a friendly smile, so I agreed, and then waited for him on the steps of the San Basilica that afternoon.

I watched the plaza and felt the heat. The air was woolen with warmth, the sun struggling grayly through the clouds. Obese pigeons toddled around, jabbing their heads for food. Tourists dragged children over the cobblestones while cameras hung like bloodless animals around their necks.

"Son-Sandra?" said a voice above me.

"Oh! Enzo," I said, startled from my wandering gaze.

He smiled, relieved.

"Sondra," I repeated, standing up.

"Yes, Sondra," he enunciated, shaking my hand. "How nice to meet you." He was attractive and astoundingly tall, with curly brown hair and a face made tender by momentary shyness.

"You too! Let's sit down."

He had brought a notebook. "For English and Italian," he explained.

His English was good, and I caught on quickly to Italian because it's so similar to Spanish. As he pronounced words and I took notes, I noticed him inching closer and closer to my body. Then he laughed at nothing, swinging an arm around my shoulder and squeezing me close. I could smell cigarettes on his clothes and feel his breath exhaling long and deep on my cheek, like he was trying to control a tension in his chest. I shifted but didn't move.

"Cena," he corrected, "is c-h. Chay-na.".

"Chay-na" I said.

He placed a hand on my knee. "Have you tried their gelato?" he said, motioning to a gelateria across the street.

"No, I haven't."

"Andiamo," he smiled.

I was not eager to spend my dwindling money, but I was hungry too, so I bought a cherry amaretto cone, and he bought a beer, chugging it quickly and tossing the can in the trash.

"Walk me?" he asked.

I hesitated, looking at the pigeons toddling at my feet, as if for inspiration. Yes, he still appeared bashful and sweet, but was clearly too hurried in getting to know me. *But I am in Italy!* I remembered, glancing up at the heat-dead streets. *And think of the stories I'll tell my friends, of this handsome stranger giving me a tour of the city.*

So I agreed, finishing the last spoonful of gelato and wiping my hands with a napkin. He snatched my hand without looking at me, guiding me down the same streets I had been wandering for a week.

"Ponte Vecchio means old bridge, right?" I asked, as we crossed it.

"Yes, yes," he agreed. I glanced at his face for clues. He was supposed to be showing me the city, but he seemed uninterested in offering any commentary.

So I looked myself, sweeping the streets with my sight, probing for new particles of significance. But Florence is drenched dry with significance. It has become a caricature of itself in order to please, its statues long muted by over-gazing.

I looked up at the sky, searching for signs. Nothing but a sun being sunk in the cement-gray mouth of evening. We passed the chalk artists beside their cut plastic bottles tipped upward in supplication, and I took a step back to see *The Mona Lisa* and *The Girl with the Pearl Earring*. Enzo tugged on my hand and kept walking, but I tried holding their expressions in my head before they vagued into memory. The Mona Lisa, with her secret held tightly between her own two lips, and The Girl with the Pearl Earring, whose expression I couldn't pin down. Seductive, afraid, intimate, shy. *She is whoever the viewer sees.* This infuriated me. *Make up your mind*, I thought, as the impression of her face faded like a wisp from my memory.

"Here," Enzo said, pulling me into a narrow alleyway. He was suddenly jammed against me, my body colding with the contact as his cigarette scent invaded me.

"What—" I exhaled, but his hand was on my lower back, the other behind my head, and he was kissing me hard and wet and reaching beneath my shirt.

A bright red poppy between the cracks of the cobblestoned wall. *Why would a poppy choose such a color?* It's just asking to be plucked, to be crushed. I closed my eyes. He unsnapped my bra as my brain wavered beneath the crush of his heat.

"Wha—No. No." I awoke with a hungering for breath, trying to push him off me. He shoved me again as I squirmed beneath him like a fly pinned against a wall, squirmed until my hand edged against his chest, shoving him away. He backed up a step, appraising me. Grinning without teeth. My eyes and face were invisible, but he stared at my hips as if they promised salvation.

"Enzo," I said, my voice trying to reach past a whisper. "I don't want to kiss you."

"You're sexy," he said, his eyes glued to the gap between my legs.

The sun like a shriveled pit sank behind his head. It rested in its flesh-colored light like a bed of refuse.

"I don't want to kiss you."

"You no like Italians?" His grin neared my face, his hands pressing my arms inward as if to shrink me.

"I don't know you," I said, my eyes fixed on that sun. "So don't kiss me."

He breathed on my cheek. Hot exhales. "Alright," he said, after a few breaths. I shoved him when he stepped back, angry for long enough to think of leaving.

"No more kissing," he repeated. "Nothing." His hands went up, in surrender. "I walk you home."

I looked at him (the poppy drooped in the wall behind him, drowsy with heat and distracting me). "Yes," I nodded.

He squeezed my hand apologetically as he led the way, but forward, not back towards the plaza where we met. "Just...scenic," he said. "Scenery, you know, through a park very popular with tourists."

"Okay," I said, and the sun kept sinking, its pink now disappeared.

When he led me up a trail, I stopped.

"I have to Skype my family."

"Later," he said, pulling my hand without glancing at me.

"Now," I said, stopping dead in my tracks.

He turned around. Laughed. "You strange," he said, "I walk you home." He reached out his hand. I took it.

The sky was now nearly devoured by blue ink, its signs disappearing.

"Here," he said, gesturing to fallen tree. "Rest with me."

I sat, looking at the darkness through the thicket of trees and wondering who would save me.

Me.

I had to run. But Enzo had only kissed me. *And it's so important to be gentle with a man's feelings.* The voices of religious women clamored up to meet me. *Men are uncontrolled as animals, but we must be patient with their urges. It's the price of their company.*

He grinned again, not showing his teeth. I said, "I'm go—" beginning to rise from the tree, but he was at me again, grabbing my hand and pulling me into his lap. He was warm and waiting, kissing my neck now, reaching beneath my shirt. "Enzo," I said, wrenching one of his hands away from me. But he was stronger.

He kissed my mouth, cutting off my speech. He wedged the other hand beneath my butt, massaging. He began to moan "Yeeeees," drawing out the "e" like the arch of a prayer. His animal moans embarrassed me.

"Stop," I said, as he moaned away from my mouth. He thrust a hand behind my head, shoving it into his face and devouring my "no" with his own tongue.

"Fifteen minutes," he whispered, his head prostrated in the curve of my neck.

"No," I said, shoving him with a hand.

"Then ten." He grabbed my arm and placed it gently behind my back, holding it in place as he reached his other hand to the button on my jeans, flipping it open easily.

I remember blinking. I remember thinking: *This is the part where the screen blurs, showing only my expression through a single eye, the music replaced by a gasp. This is the part where he rapes me.*

The atmosphere was cool now. Almost black. The trees refused to speak. They would stifle my yells, my screams. They would devour my silence. The silence is appealing now. Let it cover me coolly and make it quick.

Voices. Footsteps crunching over dead leaves, nearing. The sounds clamored in my ears like a trumpeting army, and then Enzo was off me and I was running. My pepper spray was in my hand now and I was running down the hill and out of the park.

Enzo caught up with me. I turned to see him, stunned.

"Where you go?" he said. He brushed my face with a few gentle fingers, his eyes concerned. Something seized me suddenly like a memory. *You are being crazy, Sondra. You are being rude.*

He took my hand and we continued walking. "Home?" he said.

"To the café," I replied.

We passed the chalk paintings again and I averted my eyes. *The gaze of the male is a scalpel, desperate to rape the world dry.* Give them just enough of you that they let you live on their planet. Give them just enough that they won't obliterate you.

"What's your major," I asked, watching the tourists hanging over the bridge.

"Biology."

"Oh."

"And your family lives around here?"

"No."

I was feeling apologetic, I guess, for letting his penis down. Long silences stretched their threads between us, as he looked vacantly at the buildings bruising into their cool nightgowns, clouds being draped in deepening shades of darkness. We arrived at the café where I lied that I was going to skype my family.

"Can I see you again?" he asked.

"I am leaving tomorrow," I lied.

"So sad," he said listlessly. He hugged me and turned to walk away.

I didn't stay to watch him go. I walked inside the café instead, sat at a table and placed my bag on the chair next to me. I waited five minutes before walking out, counting the salt and pepper packets in the condiments station in front of me. "*Sale*," I mouthed, reviewing my Italian lesson from that afternoon. "*Sale e pepe.*" I paused, flitted my eyes around the café. "*Sale e pepe in un bar.*"

I grabbed my bag and walked back towards the hostel. The blueish atmosphere had stiffened into black, crowding me. The stars stood wearily, their light muffled through the mouths of hungry clouds. *Is all of nature so hungry? And for what?*

I stopped at McDonald's on my way back. They had free Wi-Fi, and I needed to send an email.

"Dear—"

But what could I possibly say? David would know, then, that I need him. He would think, then, that he was right about love being a pair of warm slippers that cement themselves forever to your feet, that lock your limbs in that endless dance of saying to another fleshy sack of calcified dreams oh i love you i love you i love you until one or the other disintegrates into the blue, bursting from their flesh-sacks like a thing alive and hungry for some peace—

some peace, **some peace**.

Maybe I could find some of that some day. But not tonight. Not from David.

I deleted the email, opened up a Google Doc instead, began to write.

"Il tuo sorriso è bellissimo." I looked up to see a dark-haired man, smiling.

"I haven't been smiling," I responded, in English.

"You Spanish?"

I turned back to my screen and continued typing. But he moved in front of me, waving a hand in my face.

He transitioned into Spanish. "I'm Brazilian. I understand Spanish and speak a little."

"Bueno," I responded, "estoy ocupada."

"I'll walk you home," he said.

"No, gracias," and I was proud of myself for being so uncharacteristically rude, for not even meeting his eyes.

But he pulled up a chair next to me and sat, staring straight into the dark outside.

Long minutes passed. The hostel was only a few blocks away, and it was already late. I didn't want to chance waiting until the night was even darker, so I closed the laptop.

"Goodbye," I said firmly, as he stood up with me.

"I'll walk you home," he said again.

I slipped the laptop into my bag and pepper spray into my back pocket.

"No," I said. "I'm walking alone."

The Brazilian followed me, of course. I walked quickly and stared straight ahead. *Three blocks.*

"Marry me," the Brazilian pled, a step behind me. I was beginning to feel I was in a poorly made film, all of the men played by the same bored actor, pleading with pitiful platitudes "That smile! Those eyes!" they all gush, their performances stilted by an unoriginal script.

"Your eyes..." he claimed, "Gorgeous. I have never seen such eyes," and my stomach clenched, for just a millisecond, as David's exact shade of blue flashed before my eyes.

He chases me through the streets, I thought. Not the Brazilian, but that damned blue-eyed lover who breathes always beneath my skin.

"Marry me," the Brazilian repeated, and I said nothing, looking ahead, trying to shake the imprint of blue from my eyes.

Two blocks.

But he was lowering the bargain. "Just sex," he said, "If no marriage, just sex. Now. Tonight."

"Leave me alone," I muttered.

"Please," he begged, "You are so so much beautiful."

One block, and my pepper spray was clutched in my hand.

As soon as I saw the doors of the hostel, I raced towards the steps. But the Brazilian snatched my hand, yanking me back towards his body. I spun around to see his face—*grinning*. "Just one night," he crooned, as his hand slipped beneath my shirt to heft my hip against him. The croon was a threat. I kept his eyes locked in mine as I flipped the cap of the pepper spray.

Suddenly, a raucous clutter of laughter. A handful of girls stumbled out from the front door, drunk. He looked at them for just a glance, long enough for me to yank my hand away and run through the doors. I took the elevator to the second floor, wondering if he could find me here, if he could get in.

The room was crowded with at least a dozen bunk beds, luggage under the beds, clothes hanging on bed rails. I was alone. Everyone else must have been partying in the city, moving in crowds to avoid men like Enzo and the Brazilian. I sat on my bed and let my hair fall out of its bun, let it rest over my shoulders in waves. *Red*. I slid my fingers down a strand. *A symbol of war*. Not against men, but against the thundering cries of their sexuality, against my own thundering acquiescence.

Yet "acquiescence" is the wrong word. I want something, I realize. Just *not that*.

If they can silence me—I thought. But I let the phrase hang without the "then" because David had arrived, smiling it seemed (the subtle feeling of the very room expanding) "Do you see?" he said, gently. "Do you see how they leave you?"

I breathed; my eyes closed.

"Yes, I know."

"Come home," he said, and I was seized by the desire to cry. But I haven't cried since I was young, since I was cried clean of everything.

So I breathed into the darkness instead, breathed until sleep waved through my brain and I whispered, "David. David. Are you there?"

And the darkness resounded. And the blue of his eyes pulsed behind my eyelids. And I slept.

The next day I tied up my brown boots and walked through the sun-beaten streets, finding an open market where I bought small, sweet strawberries and snow-colored cheese. I couldn't figure out the price conversions, so I justified the cost. *A girl should splurge every once in a while*, I thought.

I sat on some cathedral steps and ate slowly, deliberately—a nibble of cheese, three strawberries. Then my appetite rebelled. I wrapped each item carefully and placed them in my backpack, pulling out my notebook instead.

It was almost noon and the sun was fierce. It refracted off the passing sunglasses, sunk into the skin, bludgeoned the long-pounded cobblestones with light. Tourists, locals. The tourists had leather bags or fashionable backpacks; the locals had brown paper bags full of vegetables and bread.

I am stupid and sensitive to be upset. It happens every day.

My fingers slid up and down my right backpack strap. I took out another strawberry, examined it. The top was yellow, specked with a thousand seeds. I put it back in its brown paper bag, tucked the bag into my backpack. Girls passed, in short shorts and open-backed shirts—tourists, I would guess from the bags. I looked down at my outfit—leggings and a loose blouse. No exposed leg, no cleavage.

Why me?

Why any of us? These questions are pointless, so I stared into the street.

And then a man walked by: blond hair and bronzed skin. His blue eyes met mine, and he smiled. I smiled back, my heart fluttering. But he didn't stop, and I was surprised by a jolt of disappointment.

If a woman is alone in a forest, and a man isn't around to grab her ass, is she still beautiful?

No more pointless questions. I focused on the cathedral steps, imagining the people who have come here, who have sought refuge or warmth from the cruelty of the world, who have sought shade. How big God looms to those who seek him from the streets.

How big loom I, I thought suddenly, and smiled.

I looked down at the strawberry, its skin overexposed in the noonday sun. I let it roll between my fingers and soften its flesh beneath my thumb as I looked into the street, my legs stretched in front of me.

Men shrink before me like they shrink before the cathedral-clad glance of God, because power and potential are born in my body, because worlds arch from my eyes.

The strawberry left clear juice on my fingers. The sun burned through my leggings, pressing itself into my flesh.

Yes, it's much more convenient to fuck the power out of me, to suck out my breath with pleasured gasps—anything to silence the poetry from these live and rounded lips, anything to stop that red, red river.

You see now why they've followed me all over Europe?

That same hungry wolf sniffing for prey, the same bargains and pleas, the same aversion to my gaze. They flee to tits and asses because a full-frontal meeting of the eyes wilts them in terror. But they don't deserve my body until they deserve my soul.

And who could deserve the ferocity of this living animal?

She swallows cities, lovers whole.

The earth wakes stark with white light, the air tastes of iron.

As I change my pad, I spot the ground with two drops of blood.

A woman's body is the origin of the symbolic, I think, as I watch the bright red spots blacken the dirt. Our blood the origin of the thought: *this must mean something.*

I imagine the first man who saw a woman bleed. *She is dying!* But the bleeding stops, she lives another month and repeats. We bleed and survive. Can a man be anything but terrified?

Then he would have made the link between bleeding and fertility. He must have gasped: monthly, she makes a sacrifice. She bleeds so that we might have life. First the purge of the uterine walls, flushed by rivers of blood. Then the re-thickening of the uterus, the birthing and deathing that proceeds from its mouth. Both genesis and apocalypse written on a woman's body.

But we can't speak of this monthly sacrifice. Not comfortably, at least. And what can't be spoken must be performed: *the return of the repressed.*

For thousands of years, doctors all over the world leeched blood and slit veins for almost every medical ailment. We moderns find it shocking that something so irrational, useless, and even dangerous could be practiced for so long and so universally.

But were humans ever meant to be rational? Rationality is possible only for separate minds which pursue objective facts, and both separation and objectivity are myths. No, individuals are neurons in The Massive Mind (earth, cultures, beliefs, bodies); our societies are synapses. We cannot be rational, but only connected. Only aware of our roles, and perhaps even conscious of the whole.

We are conscious of nearly nothing. So we slit, leeched, and bled while the ghost of the woman's body hovered in the corner of history, laughing. We'd do anything to avert our eyes from the taboo of the woman's own blood-letting body, so we soaked the earth in false menstruation. We took knives to the throats of animals, milking fertility from sacrificial blood. We blackened the soil of nations saying *this blood will birth new nations and fertilize old mythologies.*

Today, we blanch at the barbarism of the Aztec religion. But the god of democracy roams the earth, offering its human sacrifices to a ravenous god of "freedom." If it's freedom we're feeding, then why does it shape-shift in each war? Maybe the blood of foreigners is the price of maintaining ignorance at home. *Ignorance of the repressed, the oppressed, and the ignored.*

I swirl my finger over the ground, mixing the blood with the dirt.

Evil is only blindness. Sin is un-sighting.

Oppression is rarely seen, and the unseen may wander the earth, devouring freely. We refuse to look up, we refuse to look in, we refuse to look from side to side.

So, I will press this bloodied earth to your forehead.

I will anoint your eyes in order to re-sight.

Now do you see the people moving like a sea of trees? Do you see how a woman is the origin of the whole and holy?

We objectify and ignore so we don't have to worship her. Otherwise, we'd have to sit in the dirt and hum all day:

The woman giveth and the woman taketh away.
Blessed be the name of the woman.

"How is the sleeping bag?" the boy writes.

"Wonderful," I type back. "Thank you, thank you, thank you."

"Come over today," he replies, and my stomach tightens.

"Okay."

It's only 1 p.m., and the streets are silent and bathed in heat.

When he opens the door, his smile is less theatrical and more alive. Maybe the sleeping bag did mean something.

"Come," he says, and I follow him to the coffee table where the guitar leans against the couch and smoke rises from a joint.

"You look good," he says as he sits down. I would like to feel flattered, but I think he means something closer to, "Good, you're alive."

"Thanks," I say, sitting on the couch, which is covered in dog hair.

And the girlfriend? I think, trying to catch glimpses of guilt in his eyes. Maybe they have broken up. But his eyes betray nothing, and this worries me.

"Water?" he asks.

"No," I say, gesturing to my canteen.

So, he sits down too, pulling the guitar into his lap. He plays a few songs, and then I ask him about the flag hanging from so many windows—yellow and red stripes, a white star in a blue triangle.

He stops strumming; his eyes fill with flames. "The Estelada," he responds, leaning over the guitar, "For Catalan independence."

I nod slightly, not wanting to speak.

"We have *the right*," he continues, "We have our own language, our own culture and music. All we need is our own country." He sighs, leaning back and crossing his legs, and proceeds to tell me the history of Catalonia. He speaks quickly, skipping centuries, but manages to make his point. "You see how oppressed we've been? We just want to be boldly ourselves, of course."

"Of course."

"I am part of the movement, you know," he says to me, in a low, confiding voice.

I don't know what that would mean, but I say, "I don't blame you."

He leans forward again, and the brightness in his eyes pulls me closer. "You know why I speak to you in English, right?"

"To practice?"

"My English is perfect." He waves a hand. "It's because my Spanish is bad. Spaniards make fun of me."

"Oh."

There is a silence. I look at the dog, panting on the couch.

"That dog saved my life," says the boy, and I am surprised at how much he is saying, afraid that he will stop. "It was the darkest my life had ever been, and there I found him, this black puppy in a cardboard box. I don't know what…what I would have done—" he shakes his head.

"Had you not found him," I finish.

"Yes." He pauses while he looks at the dog. "I'm glad I found him."

"Me too."

"I've never met anyone as brave as you," he says.

I turn back to his face and his eyes are flames again.

"Thank you."

I walk back to the library and begin to write, but not about me, not about David, and not about the boy with the dog.

They are a poet-people, a godless people, people of conquests and revolutions, people of tangerine-soaked skies and blood-soaked earth, people of the endless washings of waves over Mediterranean sand.

I log into YouTube and find a concert clip of a young man sitting on a stool with a guitar. He is wearing a collared shirt beneath a black sweater, giving the impression of an earnest student. I can only understand a few words of his introduction, but his voice breaks and backtracks, so I assume he is nervous.

I pause the song to Google his name and read the history. This is Catalan folk singer Raimon, performing in a packed sports arena in Barcelona. Could he have known that dictator Franco had fallen into a coma on that very day? That somewhere in a hospital in Madrid, he lay on the bed where he would die? After silencing thousands of dissenters with death, he would be silenced by nature's path of non-resistance: congestive heart failure, an insultingly ordinary death. Back to YouTube, I click play, settling into my seat.

Raimon sings. He sings of lost origins and long cries for independence. He sings of an ancient silence louder than surrender, more rooted than reality. This silence resounds through the arena, into the library where I sit. The camera focuses on the shining trail of a tear as he tucks the guitar under his arm, clapping vigorously for the crowd, which is roaring something I don't understand. *But the silence*, I think.

Joan, I remember, typing the name into Google. *Joan Miró*, Catalan. I pull up an interview. Miró is an artist who sees objects moving in the quietude of their inner lives. "For me an object is alive; this cigarette, this matchbox, contain a secret life much more intense than certain humans. I see a tree, I get a shock, as if it were something breathing, talking. A tree too is something human."

I search Google images and find Blue I–III, vast canvases meant to be displayed side by side. In a massive sea, here are a spray of black dots, a tall red line followed by more black dots, and a solitary black dot floating in a barren expanse. The symbols are meant only to enlarge the blue beneath: a shade as ecstatic as a sound, as alive as a gyrating sea.

A knot gathers in my throat. I know nothing about being Catalan, about the boy's urgent whispers of independence or Raimon's voice ringing into a sea of the enraged while their dictator sleeps.

But as I look through the window to the sun-stricken streets, I think that Catalans know something about holding themselves together in the face of defeat, about identity as dignity, and the re-ordering of cramped spaces to give new colors room to breathe.

I crane my neck to see the sky, thinking of Blue II. Then I press my pen to the page.

And they have inhaled the stench of god-emptied skies. They have seen the fresh blue canvas left behind.

As I walk down La Rambla, I present a guided tour to the ghost of a lover.

This is where tourists plunge into pans of paella while the city blazes, where locals pick at tapas and drinks after the streets are engulfed by the coolness of night (here we pass the restaurants with their umbrella-shaded tables and A-frame menus selling dishes I can't afford).

And here we see a succession of tourists licking gelato on benches while wearing fedoras and panama hats. To your right, you will find children playing by a fountain— "ahh, look!" I should add, "happily!" They are not indoors, *screaming*. No, these children are beneath the blue, airing out their anxieties in the wide expanses of human share-spaces.

Oh this city has it all—and the Onyar River! Look here, they call this red metallic structure the Eiffel Bridge, built by the same architect of the Eiffel Tower. On Sunday mornings, it's crowded with booths and milling people, Africans selling selfie sticks and locals their expensive handmade crafts.

And if we cross this bridge and walk down to the bus station, we will see a sprawling concrete space where you can lay on a bench to rest, at least until security wakes you with a yell, tells you to keep moving.

And you'll keep moving, and moving, and moving, past broken Medieval buildings and scraggly cypress trees. You'll keep moving through the Pyrenees where the *tramuntana* whips through the hills and pines. You'll cross into France, Germany, Italy—

Eventually you'll stop moving because you'll have found the ending place where the sun and the earth mingle matter until one stops beating. You'll sit on this beach and watch the sun peel its layers and go wading into the sea. Long later, the stars will peek out to find the corpse still bobbing in its waving grave and will fling their cold bodies after in solidarity. With the sun still steaming and the stars still bubbling beneath the sea, the earth will release (finally) an exhale of relief.

This is how the earth and sky meet: a stretching of time, a suspension of space. Obliteration, maybe.

Is this how we meet ourselves?

Money.

A small amount was deposited into my bank account; now I can buy a hoodie for cold nights.

I stop inside a small shop where a black-haired girl eyes me as I sift through the racks. There is a small collection of books on a table (a few about independence for Catalonia), and bohemian style dresses hanging from closely packed racks.

I lift up the arm of a hoodie and push back some hangers to see the front. *Catalunya* is printed over the Estelada in slanted handwriting.

"This one," I tell the salesgirl, laying it on the counter with some cash.

Then I fold up the hoodie carefully and tuck it in my daypack. *A relic*, I think. *Of this place that burrows inside of me. Of this city that will never belong to me.*

If the boy loved me, maybe I would belong to this city. Eventually.

I wouldn't mind staying here, you know. If someone gave me a reason.

I am walking past the cathedral. It's a vague sort of morning, the sun still struggling palely with sleep. The boy's apartment is around the corner, and I feel the familiar kick to my insides. Would I see him jogging past with the dog?

But I cringe at the thought, unexpectedly. I am ugly, I have decided. Did I really write that I was pretty just a few pages ago? Pretty enough to attract Enzo and the Brazilian, I had contextualized. Maybe even pretty enough for the boy.

A convenient lie to convince myself I'm worthy of his love. He's clearly chosen the well-concealed girlfriend, the one who still goes unnamed.

Can an unnamed thing be said to exist? Yes, but we can't speak of it even in hushed voices. We can only dance around the invisible enemy. We can only evade.

The boy is evading me.

And because he has given me no physical evidence or verbal promises, I have no right to question his silence.

I am walking down La Rambla now, looking at my legs and pondering the indictment of my body. Let's start with the dark circles that pool beneath my eyes like a disease. Beneath the flowered print of my leggings, bright red bites dot the pale flesh. At the bus station, the third indictment strikes as I glimpse a series of European beauties board a long-distance bus. They glide like tanned gazelles, impossibly long and lean, as if they had ingested nothing but coffee and coastal sunshine for weeks.

Even with my rationed funds and limited food, my body could never be crammed into such narrow confines. And it angers me like a flash of oil that sizzles in the gut—the brief sting of dissatisfaction followed by a familiar hunger. A hunger to be small as a scrap of light, warming strangers without being seen, to be lost in the crack between cobblestones, in the sliver of space between lovemaking bodies, to be nothing more concrete than the exhalation of dust from a book.

The urge to be obliterated and yet held on the surface of the skin: this is the paradox of the oppressed.

I hold this word in my mouth, test its meaning. No, I don't feel *oppressed* as a woman. Just, *pressured*. To give my body to those who rate me. To ingest the idea that love is a hard-earned thing. To remember that, hard as I try, I may never be found worthy.

"Can I sit here?" I ask, motioning to a seat.

The woman looks up as if from a trance, nodding vaguely. I take the seat beside her and observe.

She looks like she lives on the streets, though her blonde hair gleams. She rests a hand on the cart next to her, which is filled with multi-sized objects, each wrapped carefully in an item of clothing. *How did she end up here?* I think.

I lift my daypack onto my lap. "I have food," I say. "Would you like some?" and I pull out a bag of crackers.

She glances at me. "You must be hungry," she says finally, looking away.

I shake my head, feeling an absurd rush of anger at the roundness of my hips. Then I hand her the crackers.

She says, "Are you sure?"

"Absolutely."

She wedges the package between two items in her cart. I could leave now, having performed an act of generosity, but I stay in my seat.

"My name is Sondra," I say, "And what's your name?"

She looks at me strangely. "Amalia."

There is a silence. "But you're not from Spain," she adds.

"No. I'm American."

"But you speak Spanish."

"Like an Argentine," I agree. "I lived there."

"Ahh," she sighs. "And America..." she adds timidly. "It's beautiful there, right? Nothing like Spain."

"A little like Spain," I say. "Spain is beautiful, too."

She shakes her head with unnatural vigor. "Bad people here," and her body begins rocking, ever so slightly. She launches into her life story, gauging my expression in subtle pauses to see if she should continue.

I know now that she is mentally ill. She tells me about a spoiled family fortune, fraternal murder, and the mafia who hunts her. She tells me about strange men who try to take her to a special home. It seems unfair that she should speak so lucidly and with such passion, and yet none of it can be true. I listen silently and nod, trying to offer, if nothing else, the gift of credibility.

But she tires quickly of her life story and suddenly wants to hear all about me. "Are you a student?" she asks, "What are you studying?" Her eyes light up with every response, though I don't offer much. What could I tell her? I just say that I have seven siblings, that I have been traveling.

"Family," she says emphatically, "is the most wonderful thing in the world."

I smile back, but I am feeling strange. I could never tell her that I, too, am sleeping outside. It would only emphasize my own freedom and her own expulsion. That she sits day after day, staring into a patch of empty space while the world rolls on without her.

Bad people here, she had said.

But there are bad people everywhere, including the me who wouldn't have talked to her if I wasn't feeling so desperately lonely.

I hug her when I leave, and she laughs, then covers her mouth as if she had made a mistake. She hugs me back.

"I'll be back to visit," I tell her.

And she nods, but her gaze is already settling back into its patch of space.

I walk to the library in the quickening heat, an image burned beneath my eyelids when I blink. A priest lays his hands over the head of a goat, whispering the sins of his people.

The library doors open with a gust of conditioned air, and I sit in an armchair and pull out my notebook, writing what I remember:

> An ancient Jewish tradition for Yom Kippur. Each year, a priest drew the sins from the people and cast them on the goat, which was then driven into the wilderness so the people could be clean. This goat is called the "azazel." In English, "the scapegoat."

We often assume the religious are superstitious, but maybe they are performance artists instead, embodying ideas which wander namelessly—dangerously—through the psyche.

"The scapegoat" is still understood as if it were only about blaming another or distracting, but scapegoating is the deepest of human needs, a ritual we are constantly performing. We cast guilt from head to head as if all human suffering were a shared belonging.

It begins with fear, moves to projection, and then we must either kill or efface. In Amalia's case, it's the fear of mental illness. But it's deeper than the desire to avoid emotional suffering or societal shame. In a culture where the brain is considered the center of consciousness, an unraveling brain is an unraveling self. To let the mentally unstable live in our midst is to face the fearful fragility of the ego. So we whisper our fears over their heads, driving them into the wilderness of the streets or locking them away where they can't be seen. We let them pale into husks of human beings, cut off from the mutual blood of society. Sometimes we toss them a coin; it's a small price to pay for the relief of looking away.

And then I think of Makono. No one stared at me when I marched through the streets with my massive survival pack—an anomaly even for foreign backpackers. But I walk with Makono beside me and the whole world turns to ogle.

I don't know about Spain, but I know America. We justified slavery and then segregation by claiming Black people were savages best kept on a tight leash. Otherwise they would murder innocent white men and impregnate pure white women. And things aren't so different today. We project our sexuality onto Black women, because we are too puritanical to face our own longings. We project our violence onto Black men, because we must distract from the reality that America is the most violent developed nation in the world. White boys shoot up schools, citizens arm themselves to go grocery shopping, and no public space is safe from the threat of random shootings. This violence roots deep in a history of indigenous cleansing and reaches like branches all over the world, with our military spending exceeding the next ten world powers combined. With those trillions of dollars spent yearly on asserting our moral superiority, we could easily improve our ailing school systems, reform criminal justice, or tackle inner-city poverty.

But we won't, because white Americans know the truth. The threat isn't Black violence; the threat is Black freedom. Their freedom is our loss of innocence. Without the mirror of blackness, we'd see that white culture is a room full of shadows and borrowed dreams. We'd be faced with the uncomfortable reality that dreams built on the backs of the oppressed must one day be re-built on the shoulders of the freed.

In my notebook, I write: *A human wants only one thing: to be seen and received. But a woman is seen only when she is sexualized. A Black person is seen only when they fit a role. And a homeless person is not seen at all.*

For this we should throw dust over our heads, should clothe ourselves in sackcloth and go wail at the Western Wall.

The next day I stop at the bend in the road, cross to a low brick wall about twenty feet from the road, crumbling and surrounded by trees.

Between a tree and the wall, I find a hole. I pull out branches and dead leaves until the hole is deep enough to fit a plastic bag with my dirty clothes and laundry soap, and another plastic bag with my toothbrush and toothpaste, shampoo, and a hairbrush. Then I slide an old Coca Cola sign over the opening that I find in the dirt, rain-damaged and bent.

I walk home only at nights, so that no one can see me when I go to the tree and uncover my plastic bag. Then I take it back to the angel fountain with me. There, I sprinkle my dirty clothes with laundry detergent and let them soak while I duck into a dark cluster of trees.

I brush my teeth and wash my face, and sometimes, strip myself of clothes and bathe hastily, drenching my body with quick, cold splashes of water from my canteens, squeezing shampoo into my palm and rubbing it into my armpits. Then I dry myself with a clean shirt and pull on a new pair of clothes.

Tonight, a police car drives past as I splash water over my body. By the time they drive by again (did they see something?) my hair is brushed, my body clothed, and my wet clothes tucked safely in a plastic bag in my backpack.

I walk defiantly onto the dirt road, as if by proving my normalcy, I claim a right to these woods. The police car rumbles past and the young officer in the passenger seat smiles at me shyly.

I nod and walk confidently ahead, going for a walk in the woods, they'll think. *Who cares if I sleep in the woods anyway? And is it a crime to wash clothes in a public fountain?* But I know I still crave the acceptance of society.

Back at camp, I drape my clothes over the bushes to dry. Hanging clothes on tree branches makes them muddy in the morning, but bushes keep them clean.

I can be practical when I need to be. I could write a book about these things.

I visit Amalia again, bringing an offering of crackers.

I don't know what kind of memory she has, so I feel relieved when she recognizes me and is happy to see me.

We chat for awhile, and then I go to the other wing of the bus station to write on a bench where I can plug my laptop into an outlet.

But I tire quickly. It's afternoon, I suppose, and I slept fitfully the night before. So I stretch my legs out on the bench and lay my head on the backpack, quickly slipping into sleep.

Then I hear the insistent jangling of keys. My eyes shoot open, and I see a security guard moving towards me. I scramble up to sitting just as she bellows that sleeping on the benches is not allowed.

"I understand," I nod meekly.

And she looks at me one last time—disdainfully, I think, before walking away.

I watch her leave, and then pull out my notebook.

But I am too tired to write, so I doodle, tracing the shape of a B over and over again while asking myself numbly—

Is a

still a bustling busy bumble bee or a brave batting bat when it is dismembered and lying in a heap?

Or is it something else entirely?

A letter is like a life, you know.

It seems to mean something when surrounded by friends and family, work or school or city.

But slowly begin dismembering your context, and look what you'll see?

THE SEA ONCE SWALLOWED ME

Not quite a chaos, but something unspeakable indeed.

SONDRA

1 pair of leggings
1 pair of jeans
3 Blouses: one white, one black, one blue and white
1 flowered dress
4 pairs of underwear, 2 Bras
3 pairs of socks
1 pair of boots
Sunglasses
A toothbrush, toothpaste
Two packets of laundry soap
Shampoo, conditioner
Hairbrush
Bandana
Knife, spoon, can opener
Survival knife
Pepper spray
A few small souvenirs from Istanbul and Italy for friends
A stuffed piglet from a boy in Istanbul
Prayer Beads
Confessions, Rousseau
The Republic, Plato
A laptop, laptop charger
An iPod
A digital camera
A small notebook
Two Canteens

I write a list of my possessions while sitting in the library, then rip it out, crumpling it in my hand. It seems irrelevant.

A few minutes later, I smooth it out again and place it in my pocket. I guess you never know when it will mean something, if a small thing may matter in the end.

Then I shut the notebook and take a Spanish novel from the shelf, struggling through the first few pages. The words are advanced, and I find myself rubbing my head.

So, I walk to the cathedral instead, my eyes scanning the streets.

No boy, no dog.

It's only two in the afternoon, but I return to camp and lay on the tarp until the sun takes me, dragging me into a heat-dead sleep.

At dawn I lay unmoving, mouthing numbers like poetry.

"Two thousand eight hundred and twenty-five," I whisper. "Five hundred sixty and nine."

It's only mildly chilly in the sleeping bag, so I am content to lay and send warmth to my toes, content to wait for the sun.

And the numbers refer to nothing, which is why I like them. Fleshless, austere, imaginary. I drop them into my mind like water in a bowl, and they roll and roll with no faces and no names. The bowl never spills out.

We could worship numbers like the Neoplatonists worshipped the cool curves of geometry.

But then what would we do with these bodies that pulse to poetry?

As soon as the sun rises, I'll abandon my numbers and roam the streets.

At the library, I abandon words and open the art books.

We should chew on old art as if the canvases were ligaments and the colors blood.

We should gnaw at the bindings of books and lap up the ink of their pages.

We should make love to the scents of specific poems.

We cannot know what's real about this world until we buckle ourselves to its flesh-scented body. Until we go there naked of knowledge and free of pre-deception. Until we descend mindfully into the material,

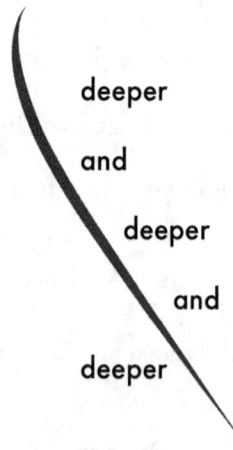

deeper

and

deeper

and

deeper

until we find the place where the material undresses,
the ground dropping.

I think a lot about the boy with the dog.

I don't think about David, because David is no *thought* thing. David is something that is breathed, and there can be no remembering where there is no forgetting.

But I can't write to David, and *good thing*. I left him for a reason, you know. Even if that reason seems an ever-shifting sense with no sound.

So I write the boy on Facebook, ask when he will be playing on the cathedral steps.

He sees it, doesn't respond.

I return to writing, throwing myself into expression and becoming more and more hopeless with words.

What good is a word beneath the white shroud of death or the white sheets of lovemaking? Who can say how this sun diffuses through the sky? Who can describe the color of anyone's eyes?

I write and delete, write and delete.

My tongue tied, my body burning, I begin painting images with red. All this feels like a ritual to expel a dimly beating pain.

I watch passersby by the cathedral steps; I want to tear their eyes from their cellphones and patch them all over the sky.

Can't you see? Can't you see? The refrain beats madly inside of me.

Some days I am cool as the curve of a circle, all soft greens and water trickling through moss. Some days I am a red mouth, hungry to swallow the world whole.

This love is all excess, of course.

Excess like the excessive Spanish sun, burning itself right down to its core, scalding skin, driving the tourists beneath their hats and finally indoors, scaring them to safety.

I am much too big for the arms of one man. I could love 105 and never fit myself inside of them.

"I'm sorry," I told David, the night before I left. "I just feel myself reaching far away from you. I can't fit myself inside this love anymore."

He said nothing, but his eyes welled up with tears, flooding the blue.

At the café I read a message from Amaya, "Superman messaged me. He wants to talk to you. What happened that night?"

I laugh when I read it. And then I shake my head, wondering how I could be so stupid, wishing I could remove him from this story without deleting a meaning.

Amaya is the friend who gave me the prayer beads. We met in Istanbul one night and stumbled on a circle of people dancing in the street. She pushed me to the center as a muscular guy in a Superman t-shirt joined in. We danced as the throng clapped. Then Superman pulled me aside, told me he was from Izmir and visiting Istanbul on business for the week. He mimed a pose and a camera clicking and nodded when I supplied "model?" I smiled at Amaya and gave him my contact information when he asked to see me again.

We met the next night by the Bosporus Sea. By the time he arrived at the square, I had already climbed all the nearby statues and stared at the black waters until my eyes crossed in hypnosis. A strange man approached me, asking my nationality. I walked back to the street without responding.

Finally, he materialized in the darkness, wearing the Superman t-shirt again, "So you would recognize me."

I smiled and led him to the biggest statue. "Can you climb that?" I asked.

"You're crazy," he laughed.

I was serious.

"I can," I replied, and took off my boots.

"No, don't! You fall!"

I scaled it easily, hanging over the general's arm with my eyebrows raised. He stepped back, murmuring something in Turkish, then English, "Crazy American."

I messaged him before agreeing to meet to clarify that I just wanted to be friends. *Then why did I meet him to begin with?* Amaya had just left—she was only in Turkey as a pit stop on her way back to the US. But I didn't need friends so desperately. Maybe it was *this* I wanted: his fear. It felt somehow vindicating.

But Superman surprised me. His face broke into a smile; he removed his shoes.

"Oh," I realized. "He likes it."

He started climbing, and I bounded down to give him a hand.

When I helped him to the top, he looked at me gleefully. "This is the big statue in Istanbul!" he yelled. "You, I first to climb."

I wasn't so sure about that, but I nodded encouragingly. We sat side by side for a moment, looking at the square gleaming with moon-glaze, smelling salt lift from the sea.

Then he pulled out his phone and began texting, his eyes wandering restlessly over the screen. I groaned softly, looking over the square again, already alone. Can anyone be still enough to *see*?

When he tucked his phone back into his pocket, he leaned towards my lips without even looking.

"No, no, no," I said. I bounded down the statue in a few leaps to where my boots waited. I pulled them on and tied the laces, began walking towards the sea.

"Sondra!" he yelled. "Where we go?"

I glanced behind to see him climbing down with difficulty, then shrugged and kept walking. There were more statues, smaller. I climbed two of them with my shoes on. He could only exhale, flabbergasted, as he watched from below.

"Let's go to the other park," he suggested, smiling eagerly.

"Why? The sea is so beautiful."

He pulled out his phone, typed something in Turkish, and then flipped the screen to me.

"Privacy," I read aloud, and shook my head.

"Wha—?" he began, and his eyes were pleading. "Park," he said, revising his expectations. "I show city."

I had begun this rendezvous by intimidating him. Now perhaps we could spend some time together in peace. So I nodded and he led the way through the streets. He tried grabbing my hand, but I had learned from Enzo, so I folded my arms instead.

I followed behind him as I looked at the streets and imagined how my life would be if I lived in a city built for beauty instead of utility. A city soaked in history. I could go for walks on my own, could—

But my thoughts were cut off by my own smile. I can't avoid the absurdity of this situation. If I really didn't want anything romantic, then why did I agree to spend time with a man who clearly had romantic intentions? Maybe I proved I could intimidate him, but why prove anything to this stranger?

I exhaled deeply, pressing my arms against my chest as I took in the old city. Sometimes the *muchness* of a place feels too heavy for me. I crave another pair of eyes to watch silently, to convince me that this beauty is as weighty as it seems.

But why is it always a man I want beside me?

Because only men matter.

The thought rises like a sudden lump in the throat. I swallow. *That's right. That's what I believe.* How could I not have recognized it before?

Because this truth was never spoken in words. Silently it seeped like water into the cracks of my childhood. Only now can I see the erosion, can smell the mold.

In the religion of my upbringing, only a man can discern the will of God for the world. The man says *thus saith the Lord* and the woman replies *amen amen*. In other words, the woman smiles, prays, and weeps words of gratitude for the man's enlightened teaching. Oh, she may teach too. But only to impart the man's commandments to other women. Thus, I moved freely in the smallest of spaces and called it liberation.

A man is a witness to reality; a woman is a witness to a man. I glanced at Superman, who was looking at his phone. Does a moment only mean something if a man shares it with me?

We women are powerful anyway, no matter our environment. But this power is diverted differently depending on what is deemed appropriate by the privileged voice of culture. In that culture, a woman could exert her power through shaming a man with his own teachings or through the subtle art of manipulation. Manipulation is acceptable only because it is power unseen. But a woman *seen* is a dangerous thing. And a single woman *seeing* could unmask everything.

I did not yet see. I was beginning to see. I was looking at Superman and thinking: *Is this why I prefer men?* I saw how these women tiptoed around the terrible fact of their own power. Sometimes they seemed barely real, recycling the words of spouses and authorities as if these second-hand opinions could be stacked into the shape of a human being.

I rebelled by spending time with the men instead, but I carried the teachings in my very own body: only a man matters. A woman means nothing unless she can edge her way into a man's story. This is how oppression thrives in disguise: We pass the lies to our children, embracing away their strength. We teach them the same old story, even when the script has run dry. We think we have long since rejected society's boundaries because we own our own thoughts and desires. *But we own nothing.* We are carried always in a larger tide.

This tide had carried me here, to a park bench with Superman, who sat and pulled me beside him. I was shaken from my thoughts and looking at him with new eyes.

He said, "You're beautiful," and I thought, *that's what the middle-aged man said who gave Amaya and I fake tattoos.* "How much for one night?" he had also said, but that part I ignored. "Okay, okay, an hour," he had revised, and as I sat beside Superman, I thought, *why are men always bargaining?*

He reached for my hand, and I didn't pull away this time. Because those religious women had taught me the third way a woman can exert her power. Be chaste, they had said. But they had also said: a man wants only one thing, while nodding to my budding body. The teaching beneath the words seeped like blood through the cracks of my body: if a man is all that matters and he wants only one thing, then I must earn my own matter-ing through sex.

Make me worthy of existing pulsed my blood, as Superman kissed me.

I kissed him back—willingly, *I think.* Of course I desire men too, but it's hard to know what I want when I need so badly to be wanted.

"I'm sorry," I said, shaking my head. "No." I stared blankly at the sidewalk, wishing I could crawl beneath the concrete.

But he took my head between his hands and kissed me again. He kept kissing and kissing and his hands were all over my body. I pushed him away. I was saying "don't" "touch" "me," my words punctuated by his gasps.

Then he put a hand against my chest, lowering me to the bench like a body. *I am a body.* Then, *like a corpse.*

"Yes, Sondra. Yes, I touch you." And he climbed over me, his body beginning to crush me. "Stay there, stay there, stay there." He began grinding his pelvis into me. Then he lifted his head to the sky, "Ahhhh" he moaned. "Yeeesss." He continued to thrust methodically. "I need!" and his mouth dropped open wide, filling with night air. He plastered his body against mine, prostrating his head into my neck. He began pulling on my leggings, trying to strip me.

"No—" I panted, between his tonguing. "No sex!"

"Yes, yes, Sondra. Yes, I must."

I tried to push him off me, but he grabbed my left arm, unperturbed. "Twenty minutes," he whispered. The bargaining still shocked me. I said nothing, trying to push him with my free arm. "Fifteen," he whispered in my ear, groping my breast with his other hand.

"No," I responded.

"Yes, yes. Ten minutes. Ten is all I need," and I am a cold fish beneath him, wanting to escape into the sea.

"Yes!" I yelled, an idea occurring to me. "Let's go somewhere more private."

"Here," he insisted, tonguing my ear.

"No, no, I have a better place."

He loosened my arm and I pushed him off of me.

"Where?" he said, as I grabbed my bag and began walking.

"Where?!" he yelled, as I walked faster.

I ignored him, practically running.

"Please, please!" he yelled desperately, jumping up to follow. "At least let me walk you home."

He wasn't concerned for my safety. He was hoping for a dark alley on the way, where he could press up against me, offer me five.

I kept walking and he kept following. "It's dangerous," he tried.

"I'm brave," I replied.

"You don't know how to get back to Besiktas."

"Easy, it's just past Ataturk's palace. I'll follow the Bosporus."

"*Why?*" he moaned, and I turned around with fire in my eyes:

"Leave." The word was meaningful, succinct. He wilted beneath my gaze, stepping back.

There was a pack of teenage boys skateboarding on the far side of the park, where it was walled in. I walked through their pack to the wall and scaled it easily, falling on my feet on the other side. I could hear the boys murmuring as I walked away, pulling out my pepper spray.

"Sondra!" he yelled, but I stayed focused ahead, feeling just a bit proud of him for remembering my name.

"I'm fine," I replied.

He caught up. "Why?" he moaned, trying to search my face, "Why do you walk alone?"

"Listen. I want you to go home. I will be fine. I promise you."

He looked a little devastated, surprising me. "I like you," he said.

I nodded, then reached out my arms and let him embrace me. "I like you too,' I said, feeling disgust lodge in my throat.

"Really?" he said. And he slid his hands up my back, pressing me to his chest.

"Mm hmm," I agreed. I was reaching for the language that would mollify him, that would let me walk free.

"I won't forget you," he said, and I realized it was working.

So I kissed him once more, offering a shy smile and swinging his arm in my hand.

"Goodbye," I said, knowing I couldn't squeeze out another lie.

And I walked away, leaving him behind.

When he was out of sight, I sat on a bench and pulled off my boots and socks, letting the cold contact my bare feet. I felt the blood beneath my body, rushing warmly, placelessly. I wanted a moment to breathe. Then I pulled them back over my feet and walked to the sea, sinking my eyes over the black waters.

Lights flashed briefly over the waves before being consumed and then re-emerging in new places. Is it the same light, snaking over and under and through the black waters? Or are the light-scraps like shards from a once-whole bulb of light, now shattered and needing to be gathered into a point? I drop questions like coins into her waves. But the sea is silent, mechanically digesting.

I won't ask the real question, not aloud at least:

Where does the pain go when we die?

does it stay in the bed as it begins to stink
does it racket through the home like a scream
do the children inherit it like a sprawling estate

And where does it go while we live?

Maybe the pain is like me, desperate to be seen in the lives of those around me. I will abandon others again and again until I can finally be free of my own abandonment. I thought of David between the bookshelves, crying. *This is what we do to love.*

And suddenly I felt angry, wanting to grip something with my hands. It's not just the fact that I run to men as if they matter more than me. It's the fact that I keep running.

It's the fact that I am pounding on the chest of every person saying *is this the door that will finally let me out is this the door that will set me free from The Scream*—

And here I am before the sea, being crushed again beneath the foam of former things. But is anything former when we speak of love or pain or any great and breaking thing?

Even now I have transitioned to the present tense when I am not in Istanbul, but in Spain—

    No—

I am not in Spain. I am split on either side of a locked door.

One me is screaming while the other stands jiggling the knob, locked out, thinking, *how can I get some fresh air to that child so she can finally breathe?*

The next day, I sat in a café in downtown Istanbul.

Superman had messaged me on Facebook, apologizing. Asking to see me again.

So he did like me. He is simply a victim of his culture, of his raging sexuality.

But my fist began clenching as I thought of responding.

No.

I wrote him back—a short sermon about respecting boundaries. I deleted him from Facebook. I closed my laptop.

God, make me a victim of nothing.

Now that is a prayer worth repeating.

I left the café and walked to the Grand Bazaar, alone.

The gray sky was loosening, nearly breaking with rain. But I needed the cool atmosphere, needed the movement of my legs. I walked through the vendor-packed streets, admiring the cheaply made tiaras, jewel-sequined bras, and countless rows of dried spices and teas.

A young boy was selling Turkish delight in dozens of flavors and varieties. I walked by, salivating to see the fat cubes of color wallowing in their sugary dust. He was chatting with an American couple, saying he was from Lebanon. They walked away with stuffed paper bags, and he turned his attention to me, offering a sample.

"Shukran," I said, and his face drew back in surprise.

"Inti btihki alearabia?"

I shook my head. "A little bit. I took a few classes in college."

"Long time since I heard those words." He fumbled with another sample.

"I don't have money with me," I apologized, but he held out two cubes on wax paper, the rose-pink gel gleaming beneath patches of sugar.

"Extra sample," he winked, "for a friend."

"Shukran kittir," I said, taking the wax paper with both my hands, bowing my head in that universal gesture of gratitude.

I placed a cube in my mouth as I walked into the empty streets and the atmosphere unseamed. The sky spilled its belly of bulbous clouds, water erupting like clear gray bile. And the candy coated the pink parameters of my mouth like a sound.

Ommmmm.

I am not a Hindu, so I can't claim the word as my own. But sometimes a word is comforting to the bones, lays lightly like cool rain.

Ommm.

But this is not a word, but an un-wording. Something to be said instead.

Om.

No—*something to be held.*

If I could hold this sound for long enough, if I could balance it between my eyes—

Maybe then I could be free of this love-hungering, could be held like water in the mouth of the sky.

SONDRA

"What happened?" Makono asks, as we walk down La Rambla.

He points to my backpack.

One strap had broken, so I wore only the other over my shoulder. I shrug, and he steers me inside a shop.

"Here," he says, pulling on the strap of a new backpack. It's a red drawstring covered in big-eyed owls. Owls are "in" these days.

"Here what?" I say, and he takes it to the register to pay. When he pulls out his wallet, I look away, because it brings an uncomfortable image to my brain.

"Do you like me?"

"What do you mean?" he asks, as we walk to a bench. "Take out your things so we can throw it away," and he tugs on my old backpack.

"I mean, are you trying to earn me or something?"

"Earn..." he shakes his head, confused. "If you need something, I buy it. Because you are my friend."

I start transferring my laptop, bag of clothes, and crackers to the new backpack, hoping he can't see through the plastic bag and wonder why I carry dirty laundry with me. Why do I feel so free around Makono, like I owe him nothing? Why does he act like he owes me his constant generosity? If sexuality is a women's currency, maybe Makono's is this: proving he is worth my time, that he can provide.

"But you don't have to," I say. "We're friends no matter what."

"I want to," he replies.

But I just smile. Because I know now that none of us know what we want. Not until we know that we live and breathe and have our being in a web of others' wanting.

He tosses the old backpack in a trash can and turns around to grin at me. "Better, huh?"

I nod, following him into a nearby restaurant for lunch.

Memories become lodged in objects too, not just bodies.

The prayer beads sway in a gust of wind, and I am fully awake now, wanting to wander.

I walk to La Rambla and find a perfume shop, spraying lavender fields and lemon trees on my wrists, inhaling with delight. I slip a free catalogue into my daypack and the salesgirl smiles wanly as I leave without buying anything.

At the mercat across the street, I buy two small jars of vanilla yogurt and walk back to camp as the dusk exhales gold over the streets, into the trees. I am hungry. Sitting on the sleeping bag, my bare feet in the dirt, I spoon yogurt as a smile resounds in my body. Then I wash the jars with water from my canteen. The water splashes onto the dirt and I inhale the scent of wet earth as the lingering tang of fermentation rolls in my mouth like a memory.

A memory.

I pull the catalogue from my daypack and rip out the last two pages. It's a two-page spread: a field of yellow flowers beneath a blue sky. And it reeks of impossibility: the perfect puffs of clouds, the over-saturated yellow of flowers I can't name, the sky a steroid-strength of blue.

I yearn for the image to be true.

I dry the yogurt jars with the end of my shirt. Then I rip two strips of field-and-sky and slide them in, the jars becoming windows of impossibility, reflecting a panoply of false memories. Barefoot in a yellow-drenched childhood, eyes turned towards the unbridled blue of freedom.

I press the jars into the mud, then lie on the sleeping bag to watch them collect the last rays of rotting sun.

What will you do when the sun rots out? I mouth. *Prepare for darkness like soured wine.*

The rain enters my dreams. I awake and roll to the sky, watching the blackness leak.

It wets my face. *I should build a shelter.* I could build a lean-to against a tree, tying the tarp with pack string. But the motivation dies as soon as the thought arises, and I turn to my jars instead.

Blink, blink, blink.

I count the closing of my eyes, the opening. I count as I watch the fields decay around the edges, watch the glass mouth swallowing one black scrap of sky, two black scraps of sky, three black scraps—

The sky unravels, and so I sleep, dreaming of plastic cups of orange juice, primary colored bowls filled with steaming oatmeal. I dream as the rain erodes.

I wake with the sun, wet. I can no longer sleep, so I emerge from the damp bag, sitting on the dirt. I close my eyes and breathe and when I open them, the veined stone stares at me.

You wouldn't understand, I think.

I look down at my hands, at the fingernails which are damnably dirty. I rub them against my leggings. Then I try to get beneath the nail with the damp end of my shirt. Nothing works; the grime leers. So I lay on my stomach in front of the stone, scraping each nail over its surface as if it were a file. The stone says nothing. But no amount of scraping approaches the dirt, so I collapse on my back and stare at the sky.

Its blue is a rebuke.

I raise up my hands and peel off the tops one by one. I peel them to far beneath the ridge of the fingernail so they can no longer collect anything. Then I examine them against the sun. Clean now, but every one of them bleeding. *Stinging*.

The quartz veins flash with sun from the corner of my eye, and I turn to face the stone.

"They were too afraid to see," I say, nodding.

See what? the stone does not say.

A smile breaks my face like an anomaly. "See *me*."

The stone says nothing. But I watch it as it glints in the sun. I watch it with corpse-like curiosity until my brain stops thinking and I remember to breathe.

My fingers sting slightly as I walk back to camp that night. It is dark already when I feel a voice say: *move*.

I don't know if it's instinct or paranoia, but I grab the sleeping bag and climb down the hill, my eyes wandering the dark woods like a probe.

SONDRA

A new place to sleep will be hard to find in this total lack of light. A rustling, a crunching of leaves makes me jolt as I walk. *Never has a night been so thick with obscurity.*

But I walk anyway, walking so long and far that I feel I have lost myself. Or my sleep. Or my reasons for leaving. Nowhere are there flat places, at least nowhere I can see.

If only I could sleep in a tree—

So I walk back. Maybe another hour, though time is playing tricks on me. I may have walked from the maze of reality into the haze of a dream.

I walk until I find the beginning of the trail, until I venture behind my first storage spot, up a hill and to the left, where the ground flattens beneath a tree. Further up the hill looms a large house, but they shouldn't be able to see me in this dark. Besides, the night will soon be slurped back into the sun, so I need to lay down the sleeping bag, to sleep some—

A sound crashes through the trees. My body tenses straight as an exclamation point: a man from the house! Come to kill me for trespassing! I pull the pepper spray from my back pocket and flip the cap aside, moving my feet apart to prepare for a fight.

But it's no human. The sound is huge but close to the ground, and soon it will be at my feet and still unseen.

A bear. It must be.

Now my heart is pounding through my chest, blood pulsing in my ears. The animal veers past me, charging down the hill, then grinds abruptly to a halt. No sound for a beat, and then a *sniff sniff*. A pawing of the ground, a charging again, and this time towards me.

I hold still and alert, pepper spray in hand, as he grinds to a stop a few feet from me and *sniff sniff.*

I am completely still, wondering if it can smell the blood pulsing in my legs, my torso, my arms, my brain—

But the bear turns around. It ambles away.

And I unroll the sleeping bag on that very spot, sleeping more deeply than you'd think.

"It was a boar," says the boy with the dog, correcting me. "Bears don't really exist in Catalonia."

He had finally responded to my message, saying that he hadn't been playing much, but I should come take a shower.

Now he's perched on the edge of the couch, the guitar leaning against his leg as he watches me dry my hair with a towel.

"Is it safe then?" I ask.

He shrugs. "Some say boars are worse than bears."

I flip my hair back and hold out the towel. "This was in the bathroom by the toilet. I was assuming—"

"Yeah, yeah, no problem," he says, "Leave it on the rack."

I take it to the bathroom, hanging it carefully and calling behind me, "It was the most blissful experience of my life," meaning the shower.

But he is behind me now, leaning against the door frame.

"I can imagine," he replies.

I meet his eyes and he begins tapping a guitar pick against the wall, nervously.

"I'll—"

"Oh, you have to go?" he says, stepping aside. "I guess I'll just see you in a few days then?"

"Yeah! Yeah, I'll just go wash my clothes." I grab my daypack.

The dog follows me to the door, and the boy unlocks the latch, holding it open. "Be safe out there," he says.

"Easy," I reply, slipping out the door, thanking him again for the shower.

As I walk towards the cathedral, I catch the faint smell of peony body wash from my skin. I wonder who it belongs to, if she is hurrying home even now, if she'll be asking why her towel is damp.

Back at camp, I decide: *the voice was paranoia*. I left and found only a boar.

So I place the sleeping bag on the worn patch of dirt between the thorn bushes, willing myself to sleep. But footsteps clamor into my consciousness and my eyelids shoot open. It must be near morning because I am covered in blueish-black sky. And there it is again: a sound by the storage tree.

Crunch crunch crunch

These are careful, definite steps—heavy as a human is heavy, self-conscious and controlled. And they are entering camp.

I reach into my back pocket for the pepper spray and slowly unzip the sleeping bag. The footsteps freeze. The human hears me.

Scare them, I think. If I stay here, they'll stumble upon me, and I'm vulnerable on the ground. If I run, they will find my camp, maybe take my things. So I slip out of the sleeping bag, clutching the pepper spray and squinting into the darkness.

I walk carefully across camp, my feet crunching over the leaves. The footsteps stop. Now they are backing away. Now stopped. I keep walking towards them, grateful for the darkness that makes me as menacing to them as they are to me.

In just a few minutes, the sky has lightened enough that I can see my storage tree, and a movement from behind. I wonder if the person sees me, my red hair wild beneath its bandana, the pepper spray poised in my hand, my body tense with adrenaline. They back away, the sound lengthening its distance by steps, and I stay rooted to my spot.

The footsteps fade: the human is gone.

I walk back to my sleeping bag and sit on top while the sky rises pinkly over my body.

It's time for a new camp spot.

I wash my face and peel the drying pair of leggings from the bushes.

They are still drenched in dew, but my legs are itching to walk so I pull them on anyway. I leave my extra things in the storage beneath the tree and take my pack and my sleeping bag on a hike.

It has to be close. Too far, and I am in the backyard of that sleepy village where old men walk their horses down cobblestoned streets.

When I pass the small church again, I take a left to the burnt forest and walk through the ash. I see a hazelnut-colored leaf in the shape of a heart, fluttering on a charred tree trunk. I pluck it from the crevice and take a picture of it against the tree. Then I take a picture of it against my hand. Then I decide that maybe it's not so significant, and I toss it aside.

I hike through the charred forest and down a hill to a place where live things still grow. Beech trees, oak, and one sturdy Aleppo pine, its tall and branching head waving in the slight breeze. There is a narrow, snaking trail here, which means danger of passing hikers. But I fight through branches and vines until I land in a clearing of pale grass surrounded by thick clusters of bushes and trees. To my left, a small gap in the bushes. I move my hand into the opening, exploring. Then I shove my pack through it, and hear it tumble for a few seconds.

I follow, clearing the bushes enough to squeeze down a hill. At the bottom, I find myself surrounded by thick, nearly impenetrable bushes in a small, L-shaped pocket. Small enough for two bodies—me and the ghost of David, perhaps—one laying horizontally to the right, and the other vertically to the left.

It's perfect.

I would leave my clothes in the previous camp's storage, which I would have to pass on my way to town, and would sleep here, beneath the church and the cemetery of trees.

Don't think the symbolism is lost on me.

Sometimes I sit in the ashes as darkness falls, thinking. But today I sit in the sun, on a fallen branch which is white but not disintegrated, like a bone holding me afloat in a sea of burnt limbs. It's strange to feel the sun igniting my body with the heat of invincibility even while it reflects the blinding white ash of once-trees.

Death is everywhere.

It's everywhere in America too, but the buildings are clean-lined and modern there, the actors botoxed and dyed, hiding the decay from our sensitive eyes. Here it cannot be escaped, and less when you sleep outside. Here, my body feels moments away from being unseamed onto the earth, as fragile as any living corpse.

A living corpse. A phrase which has hatched behind my eyes (seemingly without thought) and now lives as a hot pulsation in my brain as I walk, write, and sleep.

I have been told that there is a miniature death in every breath: the millisecond after inhale and before exhale, when we hang in the hollow spaceless.

This is another way of saying that we are all of us resurrected beings, and all of us not, our corpses sliding tight behind us in the vernix of birth.

A sudden wind dusts me with a layer of ash, smelling chalky.

I put my pen back to the page, mummifying the chalky scent into a bounded word-body.

This is another way of saying that "now" is nothing but a gathering place where the past, present, and future congeal, fester, and proliferate. To be a seer is to know that these three time-persons are a single Holy Trinity. The Holy comes not from a singular time-body, but from all three. Squatting in the gathering place. Breaking bread. Laughing.

Death, like God, is still much too big for us. If this book were bare as a clean-picked bone, each syllable would point to that desolate beauty. But a book is built of words, and words imply a Great Struggling to Understand.

Death laughs outside the boundaries of human understanding. While we huddle in libraries and houses, apartments and churches, parks and cafés, Struggling to Understand, death chomps sedately on our bones, lazy with victory.

The next evening, the skies split open with rain, pouring through the streets like it has something to say.

I run to the cathedral and take shelter beneath the covered door, pulling my notebook into my lap. *The day is fading.*

And then I pause, because I can think of nothing else except the large-lettered question: *How will I sleep?*

I can't stay beneath the cathedral—it's claimed nightly by a handful of gypsies. So I watch the cobblestones being pummeled by rain until my brain settles into a kind of apathy. I'll wait for the rain to slow. Then I'll walk home.

Suddenly, the waiting stops. I see the dog bounding around the corner, the boy trailing behind. I tuck the notebook into my backpack and lean forward. *In this rain?* The dog is already licking my face by the time the boy looks up, startled. "Oh," he says, blinking through the rain. "You."

I raise an eyebrow.

"I mean, hi."

My smile feels stiff. "It's dry here."

"Yeah," he replies, stepping beneath the door. "What are you...doing here?"

I shrug. "It's dry here."

"Yeah, yeah." The dog dashes off, and the boy stays.

"And you?" I ask.

He glances at me, and I am angry that his dark eyes still jolt me with their silent understanding.

"Well, we—Cash and I—we'll just stay in tonight and watch a movie."

He is standing close enough that I can hear him breathe, but he is looking far away now, avoiding my eyes.

"Movie night," he shrugs.

"Sounds fun," I say.

"Well," he begins, forcing a smile, "what inspiration for writing," and he makes a sweeping motion with his arm, taking in the light on the cobblestones, the trees being thrashed by wind.

I don't respond because I understand what he means.

"Well," he says. "We'd better get going."

I nod.

"Good to see you," he says.

"Yeah," I respond. And with that, they are gone.

I stay rooted to the spot, watching the rain blur the buildings. Then I sit down, pulling out the notebook to resume the page.

The boy with the dog left me in the rain.

The sentence is sufficient; there is nothing more to say. Resignation wearies my body. I extend my hand and am stunned by the coldness of the rain—

This is real.

The rain will not stop, so it's time to leave. I take my pack and begin to walk. My hair and clothes hang darkly on my body.

Tonight, I will not sleep, but will sit on top of the sleeping bag and let the rain soak into me.

It will soak out my stupidity, cleanse me of thought by its cold necessity.

I wake up burrowed in a wet sleeping bag.

I must have slept. Fifteen minutes? A few hours? My cheek brushes something slimy as I inch my head through the opening. A massive, wet slug. And another nearby, clinging to the nylon fabric. I reach out a hand for a stick, scraping them onto the dirt before climbing out.

The morning is brilliant. Shards of sun scatter like glass; leftover rain spills from leaves into the dirt. The cold light melts over my body with a subtle tingling of warmth.

I roll up the sleeping bag and pull on my clothes. I walk to the library while imagining sleeping beside my laptop when I arrive. Students in a library have such luxuries. The homeless in public places do not.

The boy has messaged me on Facebook, "Come over next week."

Apologetically, I assume. Perhaps with a pang of pity. But what can I say?

"Sounds good," I write.

Then I lay my head on the desk, seeing clouds swallow patches of sky in the darkness behind my eyes.

I lay in the sleeping bag under the dark, watching the rain shatter glassly into my jars.

I could pour the fields into my hands and store them in the daypack to keep them dry, but they are already wilted from the night before. The rain darkens the flowers a few shades, stains the skies apocalyptically.

But the droplets become drops become a flood that loosens the jars and the earth beneath, tipping the fields and then shifting into a river beneath my body. The water pulls me downhill, so I scramble out of the sleeping bag, drape its wet shape over me like a cape and grab my daypack.

I leave my shoes—they are too wet to be of use—as I slide down the hill and walk briskly towards town. The stones of the road stab the soles of my feet, so I clench my jaw until the numbness comes to relieve me of sensation.

I half run, half walk, to the gardens, where I cross through the grass and into the cobblestoned street. There I sit on some steps and massage my feet and toes. I stand up and walk, pace up and down the streets, stop and rub my feet, pace some more. My teeth chatter violently, my body shakes.

I want to go to the boy, to beg him for a place to sleep. But is my desperate situation an excuse? Might it ruin whatever friendship we have left? Another hour passes (shaking, pacing) before I give in. I walk to his apartment and ring the intercom.

After three presses of the button, he answers:

"Qui es?" His voice is husky with sleep.

"Sondra."

"Qui?!?"

A few moments later the door opens, and he is squinting at me through his sleep. "Sondra, que estas fent?"

"I'm so sorry," I say. "I am so sorr—"

"What the hell," he states, finally speaking English. "You look freezing. Come in, come in."

I follow him up the stairs and to his apartment. "Don't apologize," he mumbles as he opens the door, leading me to the living room. "You can have the couch," he says, and walks back to his bedroom.

The dog is on the couch and perks up his ears to see me. "Hey Cash," I say weakly.

I hear the boy shut the bedroom door as I analyze the couch: it's covered with dog hair. I look down at my clothes, which are sopping wet. I am still shaking with cold, so I have no choice but to take them off. There is a sheet on the couch that I wrap around my naked body, covering myself from head to toe before laying down. Wrapped in thin warmth, I quickly fall asleep to the rhythm of the dog breathing beside me.

Then the rattle of the keys in the front door. I awake still cocooned, but stay beneath the sheet — *how long did I sleep?*

There is a cacophony of female voices near the door. One of them is laughing. *The girlfriend*, I realize, and then I hear a gasp. "Ay noooo qui es? Qui es?" The girlfriend has seen me, or this body wrapped in a sheet, at least.

My heart starts pounding. *What should I do? What could I tell her?* She flips on the light switch and now I think she is speaking to me: "Quiets?"

I don't move and I don't reply. Her footsteps patter closer, and suddenly the sheet has been ripped from my head. I blink up into her make-up smudged face.

"Huhhh" she gasps, "You're the American."

"Yeah."

The boy mentioned me, then, although he never mentioned her. I don't know if she can see that I'm naked, but she drops the sheet so it re-shrouds me, turns off the light, and goes to the bedroom. Left in silence, I drop seamlessly back into sleep.

Then, the fight. I wake up to the boy yelling. I understand enough Catalan to make out a few lines. Why does she always do this—partying until early morning? He was worried sick, he said. She is still drunk, slurring, so I can't understand her complaints or justifications. The voices die down and I fall back asleep. At some murky moment in the night my eyes flutter open to see the girlfriend in her underwear, draping the sleeping bag to dry over the balcony.

Then, the sensation of sun pressing through my eyelids. I struggle to sit while keeping the sheet wrapped tight. "Good morning," I squint at the dog, who is sitting on the other side of the couch, watching me alertly. The sun is white through the curtains. Early morning, I'd guess. The smell of weed comes from the bedroom, where the boy must be awake and smoking a joint.

I shuffle to the balcony and open its doors to find the girlfriend has draped my wet clothing over the balcony, beside the sleeping bag. An unnecessary act of kindness that means she isn't threatened by me.

I peel the sleeping bag and the clothes from the railing, dressing beneath the sheet. Then I eat a can of beans from my pack and tear out a piece of paper from my notebook. There is a pen on the coffee table.

"Thanks :)," I write, and place it by the ashtray.

The dog yawns and I turn to him and smile. Then I turn back to the note, straighten it.

Time to leave.

"Goodbye," I nod to Cash. I roll up the sleeping bag and head back to the woods to assess the damage.

My storage items are still dry in their sealed plastic bags. I make the sign of the cross for that, and I'm not even Catholic.

Then I head to the new camp, where I left a pair of clothes. Wet, of course, but they would dry. I drape them lightly over the bushes, then lay out the sleeping bag and fall instantly asleep, soaking up the sun like a flesh-sponge.

A few hours later, I awake. I flip open my compact makeup mirror to find darker circles, a new pimple. I reach for my canteen and pour water into my hand, rubbing it into my face. I pat my face dry and brush on some foundation. I take a tube of lipstick from my backpack, dabbing on just a bit. And all the while I'm thinking: *that is that, then. That is that.*

It's not so bad that the girlfriend's existence is now confirmed. Now a solid barrier can exist between us, more meaningful than his evasion. He *did* mean something to me. He *does*. But where could this infatuation go? Staying in Girona would be as stupid as applying lipstick while sitting in the dirt.

I just want the boy to know—

But I stop thinking, reach for the notebook instead:

> *I just want you to know that I wanted nothing but this: to sit side by side on a beach along the Costa Brava, with our bocadillos and seltzer water, watching the sun wade its rusting rays into the sea. The dog would be playing in the distance, and maybe we'd be holding hands.*

Do you see how simple are my demands?

But the point is the understanding, the silent watching of the sun without the need to speak. That is not so simple. That is, perhaps, impossible.

I close the notebook, lean back on the sleeping bag and stare up at the sky.

Today, I will count clouds:

One, two, three.

"Cuando te veré, gitana mía?"

The message is not from the boy, but from Luca, asking about my time in Spain, wondering when he will see me again.

"I just saw you a month ago," I write. "Aren't you back in Dubai?"

He is still traveling Eastern Europe, and I look at his profile to see pictures of ex-Soviet graffiti on dilapidated buildings. "Extraño tu calor," he says, and here comes that familiar tug of attraction, the almost irrepressible urge to beg him to come back, to warm me beneath the chill of these brutal blue nights.

I close the laptop, not responding. But I smile as I walk back to camp, the memories following. We met on a flight from Istanbul to Spain, where I could tell he wasn't a Turk as soon as he approached my row and squeezed into the seat beside me. He had brown skin and serious eyes that scanned the pages of the book he exhumed from his bag. I craned my neck to glance at the cover. *Diplomacy*, by Henry Kissinger. Something David had probably read.

"What are you reading?" I asked.

He flashed the cover to me. "I like history and diplomacy, I guess." He was probably three pages in. "It's supposed to be a classic," he shrugged.

But then his eyes met mine. He smiled and closed the book.

I suppose something about flying to Spain to live in the woods had freed me into a wilder version of myself. We begun speaking Spanish and then flirting shamelessly. I teased him, we laughed, I wrote Arabic on his arm (words I have forgotten).

Soon he was looking at me, murmuring breathlessly, "How have I lived so long without knowing you?"

He moved his hand to my thigh and squeezed it gently. I glanced at the gray aisle until his hand slid from my knee. This is where I let the silence seed, vibrating the heat between us.

Finally, he spoke: "If there weren't so many people around, I would—"

I turned to him while the sentence hung unfinished between us. *Now I must hold the unbearable heat in his eyes.*

He smiled, nervous. "Never mind."

A two-hour plane ride, and Luca was falling in love with me. Guilt struck like cold water, awakening me.

"I wish it would never end," he said as the plane begun its descent, and I smiled, handing him back his book.

"Better than reading," I teased, but he was serious again.

"This has been like a dream," he insisted, as I shifted in my seat.

"Yes," I nodded.

"How can we say goodbye?" he asked, as if expecting an answer.

When the passengers began to disembark, he stood with me. He lifted my wilderness pack (eyeing it strangely) and then walked with me through the airport to the bus stop outside.

The sun, is what I remember. It was heavy as an overripe orange, its rays juicing down the white pillars of the parking garage. *What do I have to do to swallow this orb, to gulp its dark core and let its rays devour me with warmth?* In other words, a hunger: to consume or be consumed, until the pain stops ringing through my body.

Luca found the correct bus stall number, where we dropped my bags on the sidewalk. I laid my head on my survival pack and he sat behind me, leaning down to examine my face in his hands.

"How beautiful you are," he said, touching my lips.

I pulled out a brochure we had picked up in the terminal. "Look at the beaches!" I pointed at an image.

"What?" he laughed.

"They're beautiful."

"Say it again," he prodded. "*Playas. Las playas son hermosas.*"

I smiled back at him. "Hmmm...bueno, las playas—"

"Aw que lindo tu acento argentino!" and he kissed me.

He pulled back, grinning. My eyes fluttered away, to the black asphalt where a heat wave pulsated above its surface, to the airport terminal number gleaming eggshell-white in the sun. And I tilted back my head, letting the sun shower my neck with relief.

Even as my eyes closed, I could hear him breathing. He slid his fingers over my neck and kissed me again—slowly this time, exploring the red insides of my mouth.

Laughter, from boys. I opened my eyes to see a handful of teenagers with duffel bags rounding the corner. Luca pulled away and I looked down, tapping my foot in the air.

"Hm." I said, after a moment.

"Hm what?"

I studied the brochure. "You can even rent paddle boats."

"*Tonta*," he laughed, and my bus pulled up.

I rose to my feet while Luca looked suddenly confused. "I will see you?"

"When?"

"In Barcelona. Tomorrow. Please come."

"I'll have to ask the family I'm staying with," I said, turning away.

He took my hand and kissed it, looking into my eyes. "Come, *gitana mia*."

I let myself relax into a laugh. "Gypsies aren't known for their commitment skills."

But his face stayed serious. "*Come*."

He kissed me one last time before I boarded the bus. Settling in my seat, I placed my headphones over my ears and fell almost instantly into bus-stop punctuated dreams.

I should be thinking about Luca. But instead, I looked at the scenery and wrote, *The sun is in heat, spewing orangely over the vast blue earth. But is it orange? Or is it nectarine? Is it color at all?*

I lay on the ground, pen and paper in hand, noting the brutality of her colorless light.

The ground is damp beneath me. The sky stretches above, cold as a crypt, white as rage. She has offered no answers, because I have asked no questions.

"The question," I say, "lives in my body. I am here to exorcise that demon."

What demon? she stills, and I have no response, have only this pen and paper which can write nothing of The Scream that gapes always inside me.

"I'm happy," I insist.

I know that, she says.

"I am *too* happy sometimes."

Because you know you will die.

"I was happy then because I knew the pain," I correct. "Because I knew that joy is the most fragile of feelings."

Like life, she says, and I laugh, still staring at the blue-ing white, delirious with loneliness.

Then I let my laughter die. I let the silence sink.

I say, "I don't want to be obliterated."

She lets her silence seed between us, heavy with light. I imagine her mouth gaping wide, ready to swallow me like a small scrap of flesh-confetti.

And for what? For what? To become one more cell in the sky, transparent with light? And what of my body, which has recorded these wounds?

I press the pen to the page, the ink bleeding into the white.

I will not lay myself before her like the earth lays out rugs of thick grass to become pliant beneath the crush of feet. I will not be stampeded into red drink. I will not surrender to death the way the whole wide earth surrenders to the cycles of sky.

To surrender to death, she says, *is to surrender to life.*

"Nice try," I reply.

I can almost feel them beneath me, the dead once stacked like slabs of earth-meat. Now they are de-*composed* as a symphony cut free of wholeness and meaning, lying in a heap. No—less than heaps: they are particles. These bushes and trees are as corpse as they are living greens.

"I come to you now," I concede, "so I will be prepared to meet you then."

Meet me now, she says.

And I think I know what this means.

Beneath the folds of my dress, a warmth is pulsing.

I am alive, I protest, as the sky bleeds into blue.

I didn't meet Luca in Barcelona. But I messaged him on Facebook a week later: "I will be going to Budapest next weekend. Be my travel buddy?"

He responded with three heart eye emojis.

The family in Vidreres was happy to give me weekends off, but I had accidentally booked my flight for only a day in Budapest instead of two. I called the airline immediately after paying, but they refused to change the return ticket.

"Fine," I had messaged Luca, "We will have to explore all night."

I arrived five hours before Luca and began wandering Vorosmarty Square. It was silent. The marble statues gleamed beneath the oppressive purity of the sun's scattering light. I sat by a fountain and wrote, *Like an open-air cathedral, bare and beautiful as bones.*

Then I stumbled upon a gelateria where I ordered one scoop of lavender sorbet and another of lemon. At an outdoor table, I sucked out the cold and herby sweetness from a spoon, watching the people become alive in the abstract curves of lemon light.

I walked back to the square to find Zoltan, my free tour guide. He greeted me with a smile and a handshake, his twelve-year-old daughter smiling shyly from behind.

"Let's go?" He asked, and they led me first to the Doheny Street Synagogue. Zoltan pointed through the gate to some tree-shaded graves. "My grandmother is buried here. And this street,"—he tosses an arm to the right—"marked the beginning of the Jewish ghetto. Thousands were forced to move here to be kept from the rest of the city."

His words lifted into the air like ghosts, leaving imprints of the dead on the streets. We kept walking, passing tattooed locals and well-dressed foreigners. A group of girls were taking selfies with their boyfriends and laughing.

"Are they already drunk?" I smiled.

"They're probably British," he grimaced. "Beer's cheap here."

We passed a Holocaust memorial where people hung black and white photos of the dead and brought books as offerings, their pages curled with rain. Then we walked to the River Danube where brass shoes lined the bank. A woman's pump tipped onto the other in haste, children's shoes with laces freshly undone, well-worn work boots placed deliberately side by side. *This is where the Nazis told them to take off their shoes*, said the plaque. *This is where they shot them into the river*.

"Three thousand five hundred Jews were killed on these banks," Zoltan recited, and the number sharpened the water with the smell of blood.

"Oh," I replied, resisting the urge to place my hand over the river, to still the ghost of a gurgling scream.

The screams felt fresh. I remembered the philosopher Jean François Lyotard, who wrote: "Shoah devours images and words—it is the death of language." Perhaps an un-languaged scream never leaves. It lives in the breaks of their voices as the survivors speak, stumbling words on gravelly tape recordings. *Stumbling, yet still speaking.* These are images which must be described, even as the words fall flat before them. These are words which must be spoken, even if they bring us to the brink of the thinkable.

I prostrate for repentance, I thought, with a start. What a strange remembering, from a recorded tape played in a Buddhist monastery four years ago.

More tourists joined us, casting curious glances at the shoes, reading the plaque.

And still the words: *I prostrate for repentance for having harmed any living thing.*

Seoul, South Korea. I had prostrated dozens of times in the gray monastery, at 5 a.m., to the British-accented recording. The monk in charge of us weekend-stay foreigners emphasized that the monks prostrated hundreds of times each morning. "It's good for your health," he had said.

It's good for the earth, I had thought.

I turned to Zoltan. "How many in total…during the war, I mean?"

"Around half a million," he said, and his daughter nodded.

"How?" I emitted, feeling foolish immediately. "I mean, it's just so many. How…is that possible?" But I was asking the river, staring at its undulations as the blood of the dead rose in my own body.

It is me who killed them, I thought. And I don't even know what this nauseating thought means, except that I share blood with the Jewish murdered as well as the Nazi murderers. Except that maybe to be truly human is to take responsibility for everything.

"Whoever kills an innocent life, it is as if he has killed all of humankind." This is not from the recording at the Buddhist monastery, but from the Quran. It seems everyone has something to say about these murdered Jews, tossing wisdom like bodies over the cold banks of the Danube.

Everyone but God.

We stood in silence as the air cooled with dusk. Then they walked me to an ancient church, where we descended to a basement art gallery that smelled of chilled paint. As we rounded the corner into a cavernous brick room, my flesh bristled with animal compassion.

Like a malnourished bird, a bloodied Jesus hung from three wooden panels. There was something unsettling about the hanging: both a public proclamation of pain and a word with its final syllable unsaid.

We climbed to the top of the church and took pictures of the city, the sunlight waving like water over square streets. Then I thanked Zoltan and his daughter, and we parted ways.

Finally, Luca arrived. It was night now, the darkness laying lightly through carved streets. I maneuvered past gleaming metal chairs, hearing the occasional whoosh of a tablecloth. And then I saw Luca from behind. He turned swiftly as I walked towards him, like he had felt my arrival. In an instant, his arms had pulled me tightly to his chest. I exhaled with the strength of his embrace, but he continued to hold me, his heartbeat pulsing into my shoulder. His collared shirt smelt fresh yet sexy, probably a cologne named something "forbidden" and something "blue."

"Sondra," he sighed, drawing out the "o" and rolling the "r." "I had a feeling I would see this *gitana* again."

"Huh," I exhaled. "You're warm."

He laughed, pulling me back and trailing his fingers lightly across my cheek. "Are you going to show me the city?"

My eyes lit up, relieved. I took him by the hand and pulled him toward the river. "Have you seen Parliament yet?" I called over my shoulder.

"I came straight from the airport."

"Just wait."

From a distance, it looked impossibly large: a castle studded with a thousand gold windows, a halo of black birds swooping circles above the dome. Luca's mouth dropped open when it loomed into view. I smiled and took his hand, leading him to a bench so he could stare without moving.

"I'm sorry, I just—am blown away," he began. He sighed and then squeezed my hand. "And to think that I get to be here with you. It feels like a dream, or a movie, or—" he took my face between his hands and kissed me.

I kissed him back, because this was to be expected. When he pulled away, his eyes were lit by the thousand gold windows of Parliament. I didn't linger long in his gaze, but grabbed his hand and dragged him away. "We only have one night."

And the night was a blur of gold lights waving over the black waters of the Danube. We walked to a musical fountain where the water dances to classic songs, mostly in English. He took my hand. He whispered something sweet in my ear that I immediately forgot and then felt bad about forgetting.

We found the castle grounds across the bridge. "It's supposed to be closed," he gasped.

"Then we broke into a castle!" I exclaimed, running on the lawn as he chased me. I walked on the castle walls while he yelled "*loca*" from below. When he could catch me, he kissed me, pressing me hard against his forbidden-blue-scented body.

At the end of the night, we found ourselves in a park where drunk foreigners fumbled for each other's clothes. We sat on a secluded bench and I fell asleep against Luca's chest. He held me as I drifted. Then he shook me awake at the sound of my alarm. "I'll call the taxi," he whispered. "It's 4:30."

The driver pulled up. Luca kissed me one last time, passionate and long. "We'll see each other again, gitana mía," he promised, "This was the most romantic night of my life."

"Yes," I agreed. "Thank you….I mean, yes, be safe. I'll see you."

I climbed into the car and the taxi driver turned to me. "Is he coming?" "Oh no. He's staying."

As we drove away, I turned to see Luca standing in the side mirror with his arms crossed. *He's a good guy*, I thought. *He is genuine.*

The driver smiled at me through the mirror. "Your boyfriend?" he asked.

"Oh no, just a friend."

He raised his eyebrows.

The morning rose slowly through the city, climbing up through fields of grass as we passed. My head pressed against the cold window as I tried to watch, tried to stay awake. I walked through the airport like a dream and when I awoke, I was returned to Spain.

The family took me to the beach, where I laid on the warm sand and let the sun press into my skin while the girls played. I watched the eldest snack on bocadillos while the youngest ran into the waves. Back in the Spanish sun and the Mediterranean waves, it was hard to piece together Luca's face. But Budapest still burned in my brain in her bone-white light, tremulous and singular as a candle flame.

Men are finite vessels, rapacious and strange, but Budapest is big with streets and corners and cafés and people who work and waitress and walk their dogs down to the River Danube. There they sit—straight-faced as a clean leaf of paper—as they hold the names of their deceased over the black undulations: *Peter,* these people say. And *Emilia,* and *Agnes.*

A city, maybe, is deserving of my love.

After all, the Infinite must exist in our crippled bird bodies somehow, and not as I kiss Luca on the castle grounds, or jump on the bridge to see the black and gold waters moving beneath my feet—

But mundanely, humanely, as I drink tea outside a café, scribbling scraps of dialogue on a blank sheet of paper as people and pigeons pass, as the great lemon orb floods the ancient buildings and streets with illumination, as it rises to illustrate how petty are my scribblings, how small I and all these people-props appear before the harsh benevolence of its light.

Please go down to the river
and hold my name
in the hollow of your mouth.

Mouth it like a prayer
over the void beneath,
and I'll mouth yours like a plea.

This is love, I think—
to hold a name carefully

*Between the teeth,
to hold without swallowing.*

I am in Girona now, a city not bare as bones but lovely and haunted. Haunted like Amalia is haunted, with loneliness and age.

Here in Girona, I follow the canals. I sit on the blue benches. I fill my canteen with new water from an ancient fountain. And I wonder if I really could love cities instead of men, people instead of lovers.

I have crossed the Eiffel bridge, hunting for cheap bread where the South Americans live. The men here used to yell at me ("*que guapa!*") and I used to ignore them. Now I shop peacefully until I catch my reflection in the produce mirror and recoil.

My eyes.

Femininity has fled, replaced by a feral glint. My eyes are no longer soft and my body no longer loose. No wonder there are no more *whoops* and whistles. I am not a woman when I walk the streets.

I am a human, and startlingly alive.

This is what it means to become wild again: it's to peel back the niceties of society.

I have had too many of these: the niceties.

I have become one myself: a person like a platitude, pleasing and flat.

*We must be revived by the trees, which
don't apologize but grow from their*

roots and speak and speak simply, unified in the inarguable necessity of their biology.

These thoughts ring loudest when I am alone. Then why do I crave the warmth of another man? Is this whole world not enough for me?

Maybe not the world, *but a nectarine.*

They aren't filling like a can of beans, but as I stare at one, squatting in its orange skin beneath the garish lights of the *supermercat*, I can't resist. I buy it.

I sit on a bench outside, wash the fruit with a few splashes from my canteen and some loving rubs from my thumb. Droplets gleam on the bright skin. I take out my knife and cut; juice oozes as from a punctured sky.

Here is life. The sun spilling over the rugged coasts of the Mediterranean, the juice of a fruit leaking over my pink fingers, light lying through the carved streets of Budapest.

This life wasn't on that park bench, making out with Superman, even before he pushed me on my back. It wasn't with Enzo or the unmentioned others. They could offer only the crushing weight of their unlived, unloved lives.

Only the sun on cathedral steps in Florence could revive me, the small strawberries. The lights on the Bosporus Sea, a cube of Turkish delight. And now these trees. *These are steps*, I tell myself.

I am on a bench in Spain. I am eating a nectarine.

My brain stops its buzzing and my body rests in peace.

The next morning, I board a bus to Montpelier, France.

Maybe it's cheating, but I am leaving these trees to spend two nights in a stranger's bed. I'm cold and tired and found a man on Couchsurfing with good reviews. The bus ticket cost less than a hotel in Girona, and I couldn't Couchsurf here without revealing that I sleep outside the city in the woods. It would be too difficult to hide from a local I could see again.

I take photos through the window on the three-hour ride. Later, when I am home in the States, I so oversaturate the green hills that now I can only remember them by that false intensity. The man, Felix, picks me up at the bus station.

I didn't know what to expect. My host had good reviews, but his picture was blurry—a figure throwing his hands up to the sky, a nondescript monument behind him. So when someone nears me ("Ah the red hair, you must be Sondra!") and shakes my hand with an eager smile, I pull back in surprise. He is older than I expected (late fifties) and his smile reveals two wide rows of yellowed teeth.

"Let me take your bag," he offers, and then pauses.

"Just the backpack on my back," I confirm. I left the survival pack and sleeping bag at camp.

"Ahh yes. Well, come, come with me." He puts a hand on my arm and guides me to the bus, paying for both our fares.

He seems kind as he sits next to me and begins to chat, asking me about my interests with excitement. "Oh! I too love to read! We have so much in common!" he exclaims.

I am not so carried away, but he is interesting and lively and *the bed*, I remind myself. *There is certain to be a bed.*

"You aren't married, are you?" he asks suddenly.

"No."

"Hm," he shrugs, "Who knows? Maybe we should get married, eh?" He laughs a little out of tune.

And I laugh weakly in reply, looking around the bus in embarrassment.

"Are we going to your apartment?" I ask.

"Lunch first!" he proclaims. "Do you like picnics? There is a beautiful lake a few stops from here."

"Um, sure. I like nature."

"Hah! Look at that! We *do* have so much in common. What a fascinating young woman!"

"Thank you, but I should tell you that I am not interested in ... men."

"Ah of course. It is always the beautiful ones. What a waste."

"Huh?"

"The lesbians," he sighs.

I roll my eyes. "I am interested in men, just not at this moment in my life."

"Ahh, I understand. Too many heartbreaks."

"Sure," I say, and pretend to be interested in my camera, tinkering with the settings, opening and closing the lens.

The picnic is a postcard, on a green hill overlooking a lake.

We had stopped by a store to buy bread, cheeses and thick bunches of purple grapes. Also, wine. Felix had brought glasses with a picnic blanket in his backpack, just in case.

I am picking at the bread on my paper plate. He is sitting behind me, pretending to breathe in the breeze. And suddenly his hands are on my hips and his breath is in my ear and he is pulling me into his groin. "You ready for a massage?" he says. He is already kneading my shoulders with one hand, sliding the other down my back.

"Oh, oh no." I scramble to my feet. "No, I really don't like massages."

"But in France—"

"I'm American. Have you ever met an American?"

"A few, my dear."

"Well, we just aren't comfortable with touch," I claim.

"Oh, but you have never had one of my relaxing massages. You don't know until you try—"

"No. No, I am not interested, thank you."

I move to the other side of the picnic blanket, grabbing a bunch of grapes to distract me as I watch the great swath of water writhing to accommodate a thousand blue bodies in its light-tight waves. *To be here alone*, I think. Now that would be something. I could eat my bread and cheese and stare at the blue undulations in peace.

But Felix—*Felix has a bed.*

He plops down beside me on the blanket. "Would you get me some more wine, my sweet?" and he smiles, tipping his glass to illustrate the few solitary drops sliding around redly.

"Yes, of course." Since I won't let him touch me, I suppose pouring wine is the trade-off.

The bottle is tucked in the lunch bag by the tree. I walk to it, lean over, and fill up his glass. When I hand it back to him, his eyes are laughing. He downs the glass in a few gulps and hands it back to me.

"Again, please."

I nod slowly, going back to the tree and leaning over to pour—

"Just stay like that, my sweet."

I turn around, "What?"

"Just you like you were, bending over—what a view."

I swallow. "Here's your wine." I say, handing him the glass.

"I'm *serious*," he croons, "Has anyone ever told you that your ass—"

"I'll be by the lake," I say, striding down the hill and waving behind me.

My toes dig into the grass as I walk. *I am stupid, stupid, stupid*, I think. Male Couchsurfing hosts always outnumber the females, and Felix is the only option in this city. I have no money for a hotel and no back-up plans.

Back at the picnic blanket, he is waiting with a metal triangle. "Ready for your massage?"

"I told you I don't want a massage."

But he just pats the blanket beside him, and I sit down slowly. "Here," he says, rubbing a hand up my back. And he slides behind me quickly, pulling me back into his groin and resting his head over my shoulder.

"*Felix.*" I stand up to leave. He folds up the blanket and follows, unperturbed. As we walk by landscaped trees and waterfalls, he lights up a cigarette, waxing poetic. "I can't believe we just met," he muses. "And already such a connection, such closeness."

I glance at him, touching the pepper spray in my back pocket.

"There is just this bed?" I ask, as we enter his apartment.

It's a cramped studio flat—a kitchen choked with appliances and a bookcase dividing the rest of the room: record player, a small couch, and a bed. He smiles, swinging around the corner with the dramatic flourish of a man slightly drunk.

"Just the one," he winks, sidling closer and planting a kiss on my cheek.

I glare at him until his grin becomes a pout. "I'm joking, you little sour face." He grabs a lever on the wall behind him, yanking down a small bed. "Though I wouldn't mind sharing," he winks.

"No thanks." I ask for his Wi-Fi password and pull out my laptop. "Just have to send a quick email," I explain.

I email David, who responds in minutes. "Here are the phone numbers of local authorities. Write them down and find a phone if you need to. Email me first thing in the morning."

I shut the laptop when I hear footsteps from the bathroom.

"You must be tired." He emerges from behind the bookcase wearing only tight red boxer briefs.

"Uh, I guess I am," I glance away and tuck the laptop under the pillow. "Goodnight."

Felix laughs. Then he leans down to hug me.

"Stop—"

But he leans into me harder, toppling me onto my back. "Ahh goodnight hugs," he sighs. I push him until he's standing upright against the bed.

"Go to sleep," I demand.

"You're stingy" he mutters, sauntering away.

He turns out the lights. I hear him shuffling to the small bed by the other wall, and I feel myself breathing. I pull my pack from the ground into my chest, sliding the pepper spray from the pocket, feeling the cold metallic comfort in my palm as I fall asleep.

I awake to the smell of cigarette smoke and the sensation of surprise. I feel rested and a little appalled that I could sleep so soundly in a strange man's bed. But I remember no one crawling underneath the blanket. I don't even remember a dream.

A square strip of warmth on the linoleum floor: I guess it's late morning. The glass balcony door is cracked open, a newspaper on a rusting outdoor stool, a cigarette dangling in his hand. He turns around to see me, smiles. He is wearing only his red briefs and house slippers.

His face seems milder this morning, saner. He snuffs out the cigarette on a porcelain plate.

"There are pastries in the cupboard and coffee in the pot."

"Thank you," I say, hoarsely, and cough.

"You slept like an angel." Even his smile seems kinder, so I relax.

"I'm just going to use the bathroom," I point, and he sweeps a welcoming arm in assent.

I email David before I leave, tell him that everything will be fine; we are going to walk downtown. I grab a cherry Danish on our way out the door and Felix, (finally wearing pants), trails behind with a cigarette.

We spend the day browsing little shops where I have no money to spend on souvenirs, and we eat lunch in a restaurant by the town center carousel where I spend my thoughts hoping none of the servers think we're a couple. Felix approaches the topic of sex as often as he can. He is French, of course, but it seems less a subject of general interest than a personal probe. *How often, how much, would I be willing?*

I change the subject every time, at first discreetly. Then I tell him flatly: "I don't want to talk about sex with you." He calls me prudish.

"Yes," I reply, hitting on a revelation, "I'm very prudish. I don't even believe in sex outside of marriage."

He recoils in disgust but seems to believe me. He drops the subject and becomes moody, lighting cigarette after cigarette, tired of carting me around the city.

When night falls, we walk across town to visit his friend for dinner. She looks me over approvingly when the front door swings open. *"Entrez,"* she says, stepping aside and nodding at Felix.

They begin cooking, together with two other guests. But mostly they are drinking and chattering in French, only occasionally tossing me a suggestive smile or laugh. I have no idea what Felix has told them. Lucky for me, there are silhouettes of leaf-headed trees outside, swaying gently in the nighttime breeze. They feel safe and kind, reminding me of camp. Felix continues drinking while I snack on pistachios in a ceramic tray and gaze out the window longingly.

By the time we leave, he is staggering and slurring his words. But he's tired when we arrive at his apartment and passes out instantly on his bed.

I sleep well again, waking early to shower and get dressed. As I brush my wet hair, Felix wakes in a panic, says he won't be able to take me to the bus station because he is late for work.

Better for me, I think. So he gives me the names of a few stops and I grab my things. We walk out of the apartment together, and he gives me a one-armed hug goodbye.

In the gift shop where the bus stops, there are satchels filled with dried lavender sitting plumply in rows. I have to remind myself that we are in the south of France. *I would have loved this country if I were alone*, I think. *I would have loved Italy*. I smell a satchel, resting it in the palm of my hand before returning it to its shelf.

The only souvenirs I bring home are the photos: of the super-saturated green hills of the countryside, of a knotted tree I climbed in a rose garden, of branches brushing against things. These tree branches were everywhere in Montpelier, tossing leaf-shaped shadows over the walls of cream-colored cathedrals, the lettering of a café, a window set into a sandpaper-colored home.

These leaves dapple my dreams as the bus lulls me into an uneasy sleep. Felix and I are on that green hill, the leaf-shadows patterning the blanket. He is not sitting on the blanket but on the ground behind me, watching as I rise to my feet and pour the bottle of wine into the dirt.

"I will drain you of desire," I say, and the dirt thickens blackly as if choking with blood. "When I say *no*, you say—"

"Okay," he says, from behind.

I hold his gaze as I tip the mouth of the bottle towards the earth—an offering.

Back at the angel fountain, I wash my clothes until they waft lightly of soap. I wring them until they are damp and then stuff them in a plastic bag.

At my old camp spot, I roll back the rocks and the slab of wood, finding the sleeping bag still rolled tight inside. I tuck it under my arm and bring it to the small cove beneath the burnt woods. Then I drape the clothes over the bushes and lay the sleeping bag over the earth. *Home*, I think. Or something solidified into normalcy.

I go back to the library and check Facebook. The boy has messaged me, asking for his sleeping bag.

"I'm playing a concert at a campground," he writes. "You'd think they'd at least give me a sleeping bag!"

I blink at the screen, breathing. Outside the library window, the clouds thicken blackly.

I place a hand to my forehead and nod, as if he could see.

"Of course!" I type. "It's yours to begin with."

I drop it off that night, but he "isn't home," says the girlfriend, who takes the sleeping bag and tells me she'll make sure he gets it. She speaks in halting English, but when I respond in Spanish, she cuts me off, annoyed.

She is pretty, I see now, in the lamplight. She was ugly that night, whining drunkly with her makeup smeared. I see now that she is pretty, and I am ashamed for thinking the boy could have loved me.

"Thanks," I say.

She smiles stiffly and shuts the door.

David emails me one last time. "I'm glad you're okay," he writes, and I know the conversation is over.

So I shut my laptop and think in that language of awareness: university students typing and coughing over their keyboards, sun slanting goldly through windows.

But words flood back almost immediately, what I would say if I could write David back.

"I don't need you anymore," I would write. "At least, not as much as I thought I did. I am learning to love other things. I am learning—"

I close my eyes, breathe.

"Ahh, com estàs," whispers a dark-haired boy to a girl who has approached him from behind.

I shake my head, ignoring the students. "Because I don't need you," I mentally inscribe, "now I can choose you freely."

But the phrase feels stilted, as if I were quoting a philosopher whom I admire but don't fully understand. I stand up, pack my bag, and walk out the glass doors. *Walking will get him out of me*, I think.

But as I wander through cobblestoned streets, I am thinking of New York City, where David and I spent Thanksgiving in an aging Airbnb. The memories come in snapshots like a moving mosaic: wandering Times Square while eating dollar pizza on greasy napkins, watching *The Lion King* on Broadway, then Macy's Thanksgiving Day Parade while clutching boba tea in our freezing hands. We paid too much to stand over the Empire State Building and see the ant-like nature of reality. We spent hours at the Met as we inched our way through centuries and nibbled on contraband artisan chocolate from a place across the street.

And the memory that grips all others in its theme: my head on David's shoulder every night on the subway, sleeping. He knew I was exhausted from school, so he kept his arm tight around me and watched the stops while I felt his heartbeat like a metronome, structuring my sleep.

And before dropping into swaying subway dreams, I thought, *make me of this moment a material thing*. Let me weave the sensual fibers of scents, colors, and sounds into a single seamless cloth. Let that cloth reach around the totality of my body, warming me. Some memories are second skins, scenes we inhabit—seen or unseen—for the duration of our lives. If I could wear David's love like a heavy coat, maybe that old abandonment would stop clamoring coldly through my body.

In the gardens, I sit on a bench and unearth my notebook.

How much power a name holds, to evoke a person we loved/ love

Love, I write, crossing out the "d".

I know now that the past tense is a cruel deception. Anything real is now and forever engraved on our bodies. The seamed-up scream, which lives in my bloodstream. David, who has coursed through each encounter with other men, my breathless searching for the one I left. Can he (the beginning love) be the end of my searching?

I rip out the page and slide the pen into the notebook's spine, closing it. The light sinks through the blades of grass, starkening.

Over a hundred pages have passed between us, and we are still talking about me. What about you, reader? Have you loved and lost? Have you been lost?

All stories have a multitude of authors. I will write your pain and you will write mine, all of us pressing our knees into the same sea of suffering.

Here. I have left you these lines. You can say the unsayable, now. You can write the unwrite-able pain.

THE SEA ONCE SWALLOWED ME

Now wring up the words and eat them with your mouth (they have already burrowed into your bloodstream). Lay in your bed and stare out the glass window until the moon stops blue-ing up your room and the sun comes up breaking with its abrasive joy.

Collect the sun rays. Swallow those too.

Lie on your bed once more and see if the sorrow can alchemize in your veins, can become beauty, can become life.

Live off that life until life stops living off you. Until blood drains from your pretty veins and you are left cool and pale as the ash of burnt trees. (We are all burnt trees in the end— you, I, and the paper between.)

I rip the paper in half.

But it is still alive, it seems, because I can see that name on the page, the name that stirs the blood of my sleep, that makes my body tremble like an aspen leaf. Even the Catalan version fills my ears with memories, crawls through my veins like a virus, and gets caught in my throat like a thick knowing. (I heard "David" the other day as I was watching pigeons—it stained the street for hours, so I had to move until it left.)

I rip "David" right down the middle. Then I rip it twice more. Then I rip the other pieces until they are almost as small as letters, little white word-pieces ready to fly on the wind, landing on flowers and small leaves, pollinating the eyes that read them like bees.

I leave the scraps in a pile on the bench. The wind will soon lift them away. I wonder if their meanings will matter when they no longer cohere to one clear and beating word. I wonder if someone will catch a letter scrap and wonder.

I wonder as I walk back to camp. Then I stop wondering and sleep.

Or try to.

We all must end as we began, after all.

I began without a sleeping bag, and so here I pass this final week, a caterpillar pulled out of its cocoon and pressed against the dirt, the curtain and tarp pulled thinly around me.

Then I awake: *the cold*. It's still dark, but I must have slept a few hours. I reach down to massage warmth into my toes. Suddenly, an image flashes against my eyelids fully formed: my father holding my foot. My father holding my foot and crying.

The context floods back. Christmas morning, and I must have been about ten. My back was pressed against the wall of my basement bedroom. I had been crying for so many hours that my sobs now erupted in ragged gasps. I was too old to kick in doors, so I had to bracket the pain within the walls of my body—focus on controlling my breath, keeping my legs from running or my fists from pummeling. Then the door clicked open and my dad sat down beside me. He looked at the floor, grasped at the air with a hand, and found my foot (the closest part of me to him). And he cried.

I don't know what to write about this, about a grown man crying over me in compassion. I only know that as soon as his tears began, mine ended. It felt as if a piece of me had fit back into sanity, a small miracle of healing. I'm not sure what happened next (my memory preserved only that essential scrap), but I'd like to imagine that we left that bedroom together. That we rejoined the family. That the healing persisted for more than moments.

But if it had, would I be here at all, crying to a cold sky?

I look at the stars and massage my cold toes. This is the shape that aloneness takes: a sky too vast to be spoken to, a boyfriend in another country, sleeping his own sleep with his own without-me dreams. I jam my eyes shut, willing the darkness to take me. Sleep. Paroxysms of cold. Sleep. In the morning, the sun like a conquering army comes to wake me.

I don't pull the curtain over my head to shield me. It would be useless to try to sleep longer on the hard earth, so I walk to the library, where I find an email from my professor.

"The money is gone," he wrote. His research budget ran out for the summer, and he had forgotten to tell me. "Will you please still work on the project? Payment will resume in the fall." I close the email without responding.

The sun slants hot through the window, but I see gray clouds swelling in the north, threatening to drench uncovered bodies. Then I count four black birds, catapulting themselves against the clouds. Five. Six. I could sit here counting birds forever.

I rub my forehead with the back of my hand, as if erasing a memory. Then I rifle through my backpack to find the small cloth purse I bought in Istanbul. Two paper forints from Hungary and three euros. Can you buy anything with three euros these days?

I stay at the library for the remainder of the day, insisting on productivity. But it's easy to be creative when you are well-fed and nourished with sleep. Today my words limp uneasily into a Google Doc—distracted, uninspired.

Out the window, darkness eats the corpse of the sun, violet spills from the west like a freshly macerated plum.

I will visit Amalia, I think. So I take my bag and leave, and when I arrive, I give her the last of my crackers. She smiles, commenting on the sunset. I hadn't even noticed it following me, slashes of flesh-pink and bruised-blue spilling from the glass doors like a gutted watercolor.

"Me tengo que ir," I tell her. It's getting late.

I stop by a mercat on my way home, buying a Milka Oreo bar to eat as I walk. Its sweetness sickens me almost immediately, but perhaps it's a necessarily superfluous purchase: one euro down, two to go.

When I toss the wrapper in a trash can, I realize that the sunset has bled the sky of light, leaving a murky blue behind. Something catches suddenly in my throat, and my pulse quickens like a caged animal trying to sprint out of its skin. What is this, fear? No, *panic*. What is this panic and why?

My pace quickens, my eyes roaming restlessly over the city. The streets are still, like a sleeping cat, the night heaving deeply beneath. *Everything is as it should be*, I think—deathly still, ancient, blue. *Everything is fine.*

Then why this rising ride of panic, drowning out my breath?

Perhaps those Kabbalistic Jews were simply inventing mythology, but I feel the underground canals now, undeniably close beneath my feet. How precarious is this ground upon which we walk, how eager the earth to devour.

I am nearing the angel fountain; I am stumbling in the dark. The road is brown and made of dirt, as it should be, but the trees are menacing in their stillness. Where is the nocturnal shaking of their leaves? The stillness feels scripted and urgent as a treatise, if only I could read its meaning. But without the wind, there are only nouns; there is a verb missing—

I look to the sky, and suddenly I see (so this is why my body feels perched at the brink of its undoing):

the sky has broken.

Before it was blue, but now red is breaking bloodly through the clouds, suffocating the starlight in its spread.

"What is this?" I say aloud, "some kind of joke?"

I kick a bone in the ashes as I stumble through the burnt forest. The trees move like so many red seas as I plunge into the live portion of the woods, into the alcove where I sleep. Every sound seems loud as a trumpet, announcing my presence to whatever darkness is thickening around me. I carefully spread the tarp over the ground, its sound deafening in the stillness.

The red has hemorrhaged again, is spilling into new cloud-pockets. *Rains?* Maybe. *But what kind of storm could this be?* Now I'm sitting on the tarp, my eyes shifting to catch every shaping sound in the darkness.

This is the night I will die. The phrase reverberates through the hollow of my bones. *Face it, Sondra.* I lay down and brace my gaze to the sky.

God, I think, with a start. Or something churning, marvelous, and huge.

"You *never spoke*," I murmur, closing my eyes from the pain of contact. "Why do you never speak?"

Silence.

From behind my eyelids, I imagine the clouds unraveling.

I am not that which speaks. I am that which is spoken into being.

My body lights up. My blood begins to pulse.

"You are—" I begin, steadying my brain. "You are the language the trees speak."

Yes, that, God agrees.

"You are the verb—the missing meaning—and we are the branches which may or may not dance you into being."

I am also the sea.

And I cringe, thinking of the Bosporus and its numberless black beads that are nothing but particles in the body of a beast.

I am not the beast. I am the One Who Sings.

Sings what?

The gasp in the throat of each being.

In the beginning—

I spilled with joy and the earth exploded into being.

I unveil my eyes. The red-rimmed clouds integrate and disintegrate like a shroud before the great blue beyond. These clouds are the original speech. God is a syllable that was swallowed by the sea.

The sea is—

God, I mouth, tumbling into the blankness of being which befores and yet brackets our speech.

Rest in the hollow spaceless. Before the tyranny of language and the lie of linear speech.

The clouds are still shifting as I struggle to fix my eyes on the blue.

God, I say, and my eyelids cover me in a wave of sleep as the last syllable unravels in a heap.

The sun rises on my uncovered body.

I sit up, practically choking on the cool air pouring from the mouth of morning.

I'm alive. I breathe deeply.

The memory of last night lodges like a lump in my throat, embarrassing and strange. *How the nature people rave*, I think, *frothing at the margins of society.*

But the sun is out, anyways. And I go to the store where the Pakistani has pressed a blonde woman against the weatherworn stones, making out. I glance at the time: five minutes before eight. I wait around the corner, tracing my finger in a circle on the cobblestoned wall while the sun creeps warmly through the cracks.

Then I round the corner to buy a small loaf of bread, spending the last two euros. After a day of writing, I take the bread back to the trees. The sky darkens over my body, the last light stretched like atmospheric bones over the dusk-settled dirt. An explosion will soon erupt; the deepening blue will explode into red and rain through the leaves.

I take off my shoes and kneel in the dirt, digging my toes into the earth. I rip the loaf, wrapping a clean white shirt around one half and laying the other carefully in a patch of grass.

Then I break off a small piece. It lays sun-warmed in my hand, weighty like a gift. Crimson slides over my body like sky-sweat, staining the earth beneath. And I bring the bread to my mouth, gnawing hungrily.

Words swim through my brain of their own volition. *There are no great answers and no grand solutions. There are only small things that split open, revealing their seeds.*

God is not in the clouds but in the bread, and in the dirt particles that bind themselves into a firm sea beneath my feet. God is the one I trample each moment I don't press my forehead to the earth, saying *ilhumdulilah,* Praise be to God.

I press my forehead to the dirt, letting the light enwrap me like a shroud.

More food is coming.

The next day, I wander the streets at dusk.

The sun dies in layers. Cracked by the splintering day, it condenses like egg yoke as it's poured through the city's veins.

I will go to the Medieval gardens before I meet the boy and his dog on the cathedral steps. But sitting in a garden is no urgent appointment, so I meander through circulating streets, watching the dusk move vines and the hair beneath hats in its breeze.

A man walks by. And another—this one turns for a second glance and bares a grin. An elderly woman walks her Great Dane and a French couple strides arm and arm into a souvenir shop. I hear the boy whisper something in her ear as they pass; she throws back her golden head and laughs.

The bell tolls loud and deep. I am still not in the garden.

And yet my legs still move and the walls still rise around me—old walls soaked in new sounds, not the least of which are mine: the measured beating of my heart, the quiet waves of my breath, the sound of my feet meeting cobblestone.

Then, the sound of a stone-muffled chorus singing from deep beneath the city. It's impossible not to imagine the music swelling from the black waters of the canals, and I remember the words of the boy that evening. "Something that runs beneath? Doesn't that sound like death to you?"

I follow the voices like a trail of incense. The streets snake me toward the sound, the sun trailing behind in its spilled-yoke gold. I find a gated door and a rack of fliers and realize the chorus must be rising from this basement church.

I lean against the wall and listen. The last month hums in my bones as the shadows of the city flicker over my body.

What does it mean what does it mean what

The chorus sounds like what has been rustling in the trees. Part of it, at least. It's the part about God and death co-mingling in some extinct language, perhaps sharing the same sound. It is the nuns in the small church who guard the burnt forest with bleached bones. It is the Virgin Mary in the glass case, protecting all passersby with her bowed head and flaming heart. It is the Kabbalistic Jews with their underground canals and the *ommm* which lies like water beneath the architecture of reality.

But the chorus does not sing everything. Its ethereal hum shutters out the sting of sun on the skin, the dance between wind, shadows, and leaves. It does not sing the rich soil of joy beneath, nor the ripening and withering cycles of the sky.

I take a flyer to learn the name of the denomination but put it back when I realize it's written in Catalan. *Leave it nameless, then.* I leave the chorus, the voices trailing behind me like the breath of dusk.

Now I am in the garden, and the plants sigh in relief of being seen. I run my hand along a crumbling wall conquered with vines. I sit on a bright blue bench. I breathe.

What is it that stirs in these green gardens? It's not the restless shiver of soil where life concentrates in anticipation. Not seedlings preparing to be thrust from the dark earth into the bracing air of life, and not a jumble of grown plants.

No, it's not life which animates these gardens, but silence. *I am sitting in a catacomb.* The realization is a kind of relief.

I open my notebook and begin to write: *What the world calls madness is the only sanity. I came to place myself in direct conversation with Death.*

Maybe if I can allow Death to eat with me, in the dirt, sharing my beans and bread with soil-dampened fingers, if I can allow her into my garden, to sit with me squarely and matter-of-factly on a blue bench, if I can climb into her dark womb and allow her to contract me out into the bracing air of life—

Maybe then I will be brave enough to stay sane,
and by sane, I mean,
        alive,
and by alive, I mean,
        in procreative communion with Death.

The air chills with the ecstatic presence of darkness.

It has come not as sudden blackness, but as the careful reawakening of plants, as the gentle deepening of color until that color is a void until the void carries me as a body carries the breath of life through a deathen-ing world.

I hurry to meet the boy, because at least an hour has passed in the garden and he would be waiting.

I climb the cathedral stairs to find him just where we first met a month ago, turned to the dog who sniffs some people nearby.

"Vine!" yells the boy, apologizing to the tourists who look up in surprise.

"Hello," I say, and the boy spins around, smiling much too broadly.

"Well, hello! Come sit down. Cash is being a bad boy." He grabs him by the collar. "*Seu*," he commands, and the dog sits, panting happily.

I sit next to them, the stairs cold beneath my thin leggings.

"How are you?" he asks, watching the tourists below, avoiding my eyes.

I was walking in the darkness just moments before, the air prickling with the presence of stars. And in me pulsed the red knowing that I am alive.

I can't describe these things to the boy, so I just nod. "Good," I say. "It's a beautiful night."

"Any more boars?"

"One, last night, in the trees. He snorted and pawed the ground but didn't charge, so I just kept walking."

The boy laughs a little, looking at his hands. "You're brave," he says again.

I shake my head. Silence punctuates the space between us.

"Well," he says, "I can't stay long. I should go eat dinner with my girlfriend." He pats me on the leg. It's the first time he has admitted it: "my girlfriend." The word is a weight on his voice.

I look down without responding, the stones gleaming like washed bones beneath our feet. *We are bathed in the same sky*, I think. We are bound by the same atmosphere which bifurcates our bodies. Somehow, this distance between our feet is a shared belonging.

"Good," I say, nodding.

"She never comes out with me and the dog," he says, not standing up yet. "She says he is mine and I should take care of him."

"Hm," I say.

"She doesn't much like dogs."

I don't respond.

"We kind of broke up," he says. "Things have been hard."

"Do you love her?" I ask.

"Yes."

"Is it worth it?"

"Yes. *Absolutely* yes."

"Good," I say, shrugging my shoulders.

A silence.

"Yeah. Yeah, I really love her."

I look at him, and his eyes finally lock into mine. They are pleading.

And still I linger, thinking of the night I stood near these steps and first saw them: the boy and his dog, locked in their playful dance. His wide smile of accommodation as I asked for his help, the easy conversation as the space between our walking bodies tensed with attraction, and then the shared understanding in that lamplit glance. I'd felt the universe break its body into a shimmy, felt it shake the time-and-space coded blocks of people, places, and things just so he and I could meet.

If we would have chosen to be together, in spite of everything, if we would have plunged into the irrational religion of romantic love, I would mention that lamplit look every time we told and retold the story. "And that's when I knew," I would say softly, and he would smile at me adoringly, jumping in, "I mean, think of the odds! Two people just following their dreams and meeting each other along the way. She knew, didn't you, honey? Remember what you told me about Girona?"

"Oh," I would blush, "just that I looked at a lot of cities in the area, you know, but something about Girona…" And here I would shrug. "It was like he was calling me."

If we would have chosen to be together, all this would mean something like destiny.

Instead, the boy stands and tugs at the leash.

"Let's go," to the dog.

"It was good to see you, Sergi," I say, and he nods.

"Have a good night," he calls as he walks away.

"Goodnight," I say, to the stones beneath me.

And left to my silence, I can finally breathe.

I spend the rest of the night in the library, knitting words into sloppy sentences, lopsided paragraphs. Sometimes, the words make everything clear—a bright unveiling of sun in the salamander gray of waters.

I flip to an old notebook page and cock my head to the side, thinking: *beneath the roots lies not rich soil, but the great white salt of disintegration: a sea.*

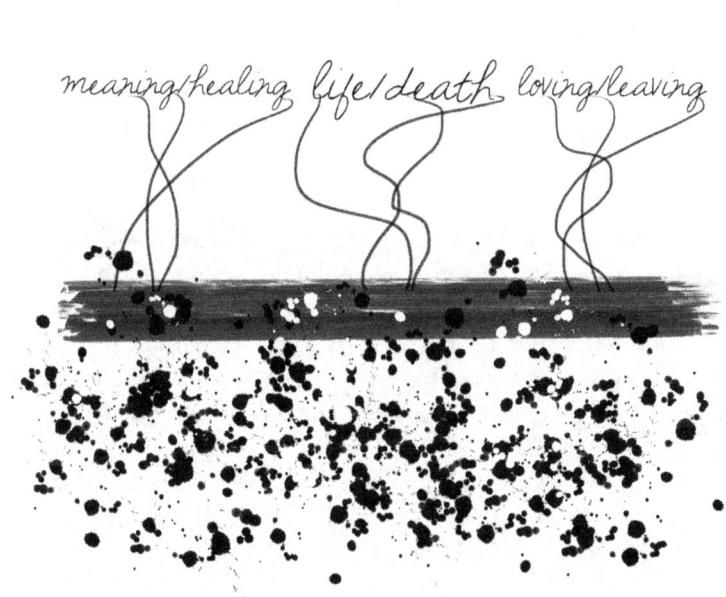

A security guard ambles up to me at closing. I smile and tuck my laptop in my backpack. *Just like a university student*, I think, although he speaks to me in Catalan ("Ets estudiant aquí?") and I am forced to respond in Spanish, "No, not at this university." He raises an eyebrow; sometimes speaking Spanish in Catalonia feels like a political statement.

I stand and squeeze past him, back to the still night streets—alone now, and eagerly awaiting some sleep.

In the morning, the hunger.

It follows me into the afternoon, hollowing my stomach and starving my writing clean of substance. I try to imagine myself as a wandering ascetic, focusing on the pang of hunger as if it were a trained intention. Sometimes renaming a thing can release you from its gnawing.

But it doesn't help—I am not a wandering ascetic. I'm an impractical girl who is hungry for the sake of stupidity. My professor didn't know I was stranded in Europe, and I had made no backup plan.

Makono doesn't know about the hunger, but he hugs me warmly when he sees me, grabs my daypack to shoulder it himself, and leads me across a street to a restaurant. He orders me two sandwiches and then shrewdly watches me eat. I try not to devour too greedily, even casually leaving the last bite on my plate for a few minutes before succumbing to the seduction and popping it in my mouth.

After lunch, we walk the streets for hours, talking and laughing and sitting on benches, watching the birds. A Danish family asks us for directions and Makono takes them exactly where they need to be while I trail behind.

"How do you know Girona so well?" I ask him. "I walk these streets all the time and still get lost."

"That's because you're too much in your head." I don't deny this, as I was even then thinking of the importance of speaking in circles, seeing as the center drops out when we approach reality directly.

We walk to La Rambla, and soon he is claiming hunger again. "Let's try someplace new," he says, and leads me into a restaurant I had often passed but never thought of entering. We are seated next to an expensive-looking couple that speaks in a mixture of French and English to their two blonde children.

"Makono," I whisper, leaning forward. "The other restaurants are fine. Why so fancy?"

A waiter hands us two menus and raises a careful eyebrow at Makono, who pretends not to notice.

"You deserve the best," he states, and proceeds to order, asking the waiter for half a chicken.

"Ah, with wild mushrooms and thyme?"

"Sí, pollo," Makono repeats, uninterested in the details.

The waiter turns to me—sympathetically, it seems.

"Um yes, I will have the five cheese gnocchi please."

"Ahh," moans Makono, clucking his tongue. "Are you a bird? Order something else too, like this," and he points to the menu, at a picture of beef.

"Gnocchi," I say firmly, to the waiter. To Makono, I shrug.

"It's my favorite."

The waiter takes our menus and brings back a coke for Makono, a water for me. When our food arrives, he forces me to eat a few bites of his chicken, and then we sit for two more hours while I start to get antsy.

Makono isn't used to hurrying, but the waiter keeps coming back to our table, his "What else can I help you with?" sounding less and less vaguely like a threat.

"Let's leave and see the fortifications," I suggest.

"Again?" he groans.

"You know, Makono," I begin. "This is my last week."

We haven't talked about my leaving, so I'm surprised when he looks at me without responding, sipping his coke. I raise an eyebrow.

"I know," he says, shrugging. "What day?"

"I'm not sure. I'm trying to find a place to stay in Barcelona the night before."

He waves at the waiter, who hurries over and hands him the check.

"Hurry," he says, grabbing my daypack and throwing it over his shoulder.

I follow him out of the restaurant to the heat-stricken streets. We walk towards the old part of the city. "You're quiet," I mumble, but he doesn't hear me, is scanning the streets like he's looking for something. Suddenly he grabs my hand and pulls me inside a small store. I blink my eyes and see the Pakistani owner.

"Ah, Mali!" he yells. Apparently, they know each other. "Always glad to see another Muslim!" Makono smiles broadly as they shake hands.

Then he turns to me. "We're here to buy you food."

I shake my head. "Don't be ridiculous, Makono. I don't need food."

According to the story I have told him, this is true. I'm a wealthy American with a weekly allowance from the mysterious family who hosts me. Why would he think otherwise?

He places some beef jerky and chocolate bars in the basket, some pre-packaged meals. "I am buying you food," he says, picking up a watermelon and moving the chocolate bars to make room in the basket. "Either you choose it yourself or I choose it for you."

"Makono..."

He turns to meet my eyes. "Sondra, *I mean it*. We're not leaving until this basket is full."

So I put the beef jerky back on a shelf and grab a package of crackers instead. He nods, and soon we have filled the basket. We leave the store with five bags of food, so many that he struggles to carry them (and won't let me help) as I take him back to the bus station.

When we get there, he carefully rearranges the food in my backpack, handing me the rest to carry. "Are you sure you'll be alright with all these bags?" he asks.

I nod. He is folding a bill between his fingers—his bus fare, I assume.

"Makono," I start. "I can't tell you how much this means to—"

But he waves a hand, impatient. "You're my friend," he says.

"I'll see you soon," I say, stepping forward to embrace him. His arms assent, wrapping my body easily. Then he tightens me against his chest, breathing into my shoulder.

When his bus pulls away, I open the backpack and rummage for my pepper spray.

In the pocket where I keep loose change, I find a twenty-euro bill, folded carefully.

I take the food back to camp and bury some of it in storage, packing it carefully with bags.

I eat the watermelon first, all in one day.

My hands are wet with its clear, sweet juice. I take a picture of it with my camera. I raise it to the sky to see the red gleam against the wispy blue. I pick out the seeds and rub them in my hands, then I lay on the ground as bloated as a corpse.

The chocolate I save. One is plain dark, and the other has hazelnuts. I pack the crackers in my daypack, for when I get hungry at the library. I put the beans in my second camp spot, so they're accessible at mornings or nights. These are simple things, but they feel like everything.

With these bags of food, Makono has restored me, and I can return to the library to write.

The next morning, I visit Amalia, bringing the bar of chocolate with hazelnuts.

"I've missed you," she says.

"How have you done with the rains?"

"The alleyway is covered," she shrugs.

We sit together while she eats, and she asks if I miss my family.

"Of course," I say. "I miss my boyfriend, too," meaning David, who is not my boyfriend.

"Yes, yes, you are too beautiful to be alone. I was beautiful once too, you know."

"You are beautiful now," I say, and I mean it.

"No, no," she shakes her head. "Everyone is ugly on the streets."

I change the subject, joke about Trump. Rumors were starting that he would run for president, and the Spaniards thought it was hilarious.

She loves to hear about America; she used to see it all the time on TV. "A beautiful country," she keeps saying. "Just beautiful."

"Yes," I agree, but the darkness is deepening, so I leave her with the chocolate and begin walking home.

The next day smolders with sun.

I have taken a bus to Vidreres, as promised, to meet Makono's house full of cousins. When I step off the bus, he rises from the bench to greet me. I am enveloped in the masculine smell of his cologne and the crisp blue of his button-up shirt.

"You look nice," I comment, instinctively.

He clicks his tongue, grabbing my bag and walking ahead.

"I'm leaving Monday afternoon," I say, catching up.

"You're not coming back," he states.

"I might," I reply, because I am not stupid enough to lie.

"No," he says. "I dreamt it. And my dreams are always right."

I don't respond, letting the silence sink between us as we walk.

Then he takes a quick right, striding inside a store. "It's an Italian company," he whispers as my eyes adjust to the artificial light. Shelves of shoes line the walls, their toes and curved heels gleaming as though the leather skins were still alive. I reach out to touch a pair of sandals, rubbing a strap until my thumb is warm with the smell of skin.

"These sandals were made to last," says a woman's voice, and I turn see a well-dressed sales attendant, smiling.

"Oh, I'm just looking."

"We're here to buy her shoes," Makono interrupts. "She's a size—what size are you?"

I glare at him, feeling a blush begin to burn through my body. "I don't need shoes," I whisper through my teeth.

He smiles, leaning towards me. "Just like you didn't need food?"

And the blush deepens. I shrink like a child whose secret escapades have been known by her chuckling parents all along.

"Size?" the saleswoman repeats, her smile tightening.

I raise my eyes. "I'm a size ten. But I'll need to see the European sizes."

He buys me a pair of shoes which I take to a nearby bench, pulling off my boots and strapping on the sandals with a barely suppressed smile.

"They're nice," he says.

I nod, wriggling my toes to feel the leather beneath. "They're so soft."

He picks up my boots and puts them in the shopping bag. "Let's go."

But I'm rooted to the bench. I feel like my "thank yous" have run out, leaving room for only unease. "I didn't want you to buy them," I say, knowing it would sound ungrateful, but not knowing what else to say.

"It's nothing," he shrugs. "No more thank yous."

I stand up, watching my feet as we walk to the apartment. There five or six cousins greet me with nods and shy smiles. One of them makes lunch—chicken breasts swimming in tomatoes and spices. We dive into the baking sheet with our hands while watching an African soap opera on a bulky TV. Then they clear the table, insisting I stay in my seat. Makono asks if I want to shower or take a nap.

"You look tired," he states.

"I'll just take a shower, if you don't mind."

He leads me upstairs where there is a change of clothes on the bed.

"Where'd you get these?" I ask, lifting up the edge of a silk blouse.

"Downstairs. I buy clothes for my family in Mali." Then he gestures to a folded towel, soap, and a pink razor on the nightstand. "These are also for you."

He leaves me to my privacy, closing the door behind him.

And I shower, vigorously scrubbing my body with the citrus-smelling soap as if to cleanse myself of guilt. I haven't led him on, I think. I've been careful about that. But accepting his gifts feels wrong, like he is paying the price of my own self-encounter. And if others are paying the price, is it really *me* that I'm encountering?

I dry myself and dress in the new clothes, which fit perfectly. The room is quiet and the curtains thick to keep out the afternoon sun. I walk to the bed as if drawn by a dream, collapsing on the comforter and falling instantly asleep.

"It's late."

I jolt awake. Makono is sitting next to me on the bed. The room is dark, the sun no longer fighting through the curtains. "What," I mumble, sitting up.

"It's late," he repeats. "Are you staying here or going back to Girona?"

In the groggy warmth of the space after sleep, I can only see Makono abstractly. His body is sketched hazily, but his eyes are like the backs of beetles—hard-edged and glinting with an unnamable light. I want to touch his face to smooth away the glint, but I'm afraid of tenderness intruding between us on this bed.

"Can I tell you something?" I whisper.

I didn't plan to do this, but it's too late to retreat, the words already tensing the air between us. He reaches for a glass of water on the nightstand, handing it to me. I take a sip while staring into my lap.

"Tell me," he says.

"I've been sleeping outside," I reply, placing the glass on the nightstand. I stare at the far wall instead of his face. The silence has stretched the room, and I feel it between us like a pair of eyes. I keep my gaze on the wall, waiting for some peripheral voice to reply.

"You lied to me." His voice sounds wrong. *Thin.* Maybe I have not woken. Maybe this is a dream and, in this dream, Makono is in love with me.

I shake my head. "I didn't lie to you." But then I realize that I had. I had told him about the family, about teaching English. "I had to lie to you," I revise. "I lied to everyone so they wouldn't keep me back. You would have tried to stop me."

"Why did you do it?" he asks. I want to offer him water for the dryness in his voice, but that would mean grazing his line of sight.

"It was *a choice*," I emphasize. "I had to. I am...writing a book. I didn't want to sle—"

He is crying.

I turn to him and his shoulders are shaking, and he is staring at the other wall and biting his fist so the tears won't erupt in a sob. I grip his shoulders with my hands and search his eyes. I need evidence that the tears are washing away that dangerous glint, that we can settle back into friendship.

"I'm sorry," I say, but I am addressing the tears on his cheeks and not his eyes, which are still fixed defiantly on the other wall.

"Stop! I'm sorry."

"Stupid, stupid girl," he whispers, and now there is anger, his jaw tensing. "You could have been *killed*. You could have been *raped*."

"But it's over now!" I exclaim, laughing stupidly. "I leave in two days."

His tears have stopped. His fist has released and is rubbing his thigh, his other hand wiping his eyes. "You are staying with my cousins in Girona," he states, his eyes on the bed.

"No. I am perfectly safe, I promise. I'm staying outside."

He looks up with such ferocity of compassion that I recoil.

"What do you—" I stammer.

"You are not sleeping outside for another night," he says calmly.

There will be no argument, I think.

So I nod, swallowing. "Okay."

I hand him the glass of water, and we leave the bedroom together, taking the last bus back to Girona.

I awake the next morning as new as a child.

In the bedroom they set aside for me, the sun suffuses through the white curtain with a dandelion tinted light. *Is this what summer feels like when you're a child? The world wakes with you, innocent and sane.* I close my eyes and breathe into the laundry scent of the pillowcase.

A gentle knock at the door. Makono comes in, sits on the bed. "How did you sleep?"

I smile widely. "Bien. Súper bien."

He smiles too, but with a note of unease.

"Did you sleep—" I start.

"Oh, yes," he says, waving a hand dismissively. "Good. Your women things are in the bathroom."

"Women…things?"

"A brush. Lotion. Lady things." He enunciates clearly, as if my Spanish had lapsed.

"Ahhh, thank you," I pat his hand and head towards the bathroom.

"And your breakfast is in the kitchen," he calls after me. "By the stove."

I glance at him. "Why? I can—"

But he waves his hand again, so I close the door. The brush still has a tag on it; he must have bought the "lady things" this morning.

After I shower and brush my hair, Makono makes me herbal tea with milk and warms bread with chicken in the microwave. I tell him I have a milk sensitivity, but he doesn't understand. "Milk is good for you," he insists, so I drink a few careful sips, dumping it in the sink when he isn't looking.

For lunch, he warms up leftovers from last night's dinner and scoops huge portions onto my plate, insisting that I eat more, that I need to fatten up, "like you were in Italy." He shows me a picture from my Facebook. I am chopping vegetables on the sailboat, my back (and butt) to the camera. "It's the angle," I insist. "No, no, no," he chides, clicking his tongue, "You were nice and fat."

While I eat, he goes into the bedroom to make my bed. I try to clean when the cousins aren't looking, because if they see me, they click their tongues and make me sit down again. I'm not sure how many men live here. Some are always going, and more are always coming, and they all call each other "cousin," though I'm not sure they're related.

It's remarkably clean anyway, and I can't help but be surprised that a house full of men so soundly defies the stereotype. Everyone puts things away quietly, cleaning up spills, folding up blankets into neat little squares. I try to make myself unobtrusive, so I watch TV with them, talk with them, sit and listen as they speak in Spanish or Mali.

Makono watches TV with us too, sitting near me but not too near. Car racing is his cousin's favorite channel. He glances at me often to gauge my reaction, not wanting to bore me. I'm bored anyway, so I smile faintly when I feel his eyes.

"Come with me," says Makono, and I follow him out the front door. His cousins turn to watch us leave.

"Mercado," Makono explains and they nod, pivoting back to the screen.

We buy bread and some red sauce at a corner market. He asks if I want cookies. "No, just food." I offer to cook, and he shakes his head. Back in his cousin's apartment building, he guides me to the elevator with his hand on my back.

I look up and he looks away, ashamed. Shakes his head. "Thank you," I say, though I am not sure why. The elevator dings and we get off on the fifth floor. Makono walks ahead, opening the door and standing aside for me to pass.

He places the groceries on the kitchen counter and I sit back on the couch near his cousin, watching the cars race with glazed eyes.

I am sitting on the bed with my laptop open, forwarding my itinerary to my mom.

Two gentle knocks on the door.

"Pasa," I call, and Makono enters.

I shut my laptop and gesture to the bed, where he sits stiffly, smoothing the lines on the comforter.

"Are you okay?" I ask, interrupting the silence that is beginning to feel foreboding.

"Sondra..." His voice is defeated; he takes a shuddering breath.

"I don't want to ask this."

I nod. "Then don't."

He meets my eyes for just a moment, then lowers them again, studying his hands. "You'll say 'no,'" he says, pressing his palms into the bed.

I wait, staring at his hands as they tense and release.

"You can come back, and I can marry y—"

"No," I say. "No."

"I know, I know. But think about it. *Please* think about it."

"I can't. We're too different, Makono. We have different lives. It could never—"

He shakes his head at his hands. "I'll never meet another woman like you."

I place my hand on his back, feel it rising beneath my palm as he breathes. "Never," he insists, vigorously shaking his head.

"You *will*."

"Never, never, never." He buries his face in his hands.

Where does the love go when we die?

does it blister in our bones until they crack like aged stones
in the sulfuric caves of the earth

does it stay red in the blood of our children,
wet in the salt of their eyes

like the sting of a promise, unsatisfied?

May no love be lost. The phrase recites itself silently as Makono walks beside me. **May no love be lost.**

We are on the road to my first camp spot, where I need to gather my things. I had told him, "Mejor que te quedes," suggesting that he stay.

But this angered him. "You don't trust me!" So I agreed to take him, and now he looks around as we pass the synagogue and then the gardens.

"You live here?" The concern softens his voice.

"Close," I say curtly.

When we start on the dirt road, I say, "Just a moment." I run to storage number one to exhume my dirty laundry, soap, and shampoo, sliding the Coca Cola sign back over the hole.

When I come back, he is frozen on the road. "What?" I ask.

He shakes his head.

"Are you going to do this again?"

"*Why* didn't you tell me?" The anger is back.

"Ugh," I charge down the road by myself. "You're impossible."

"You could have stayed with my cousin!" he yells, striding after me. "You didn't have to live like this!"

"Makono, I've told you a thousand times, *I chose* to live like this."

"You don't trust me," he insists. "You *don't*."

I ignore him. When we get to the power line, I say, "We're here. Are you going to wait on the road?"

His arms are crossed over his chest, but he shakes his head firmly. "I'm coming."

"Just watch out for the thorn bushes," I mumble.

When we arrive at my clearing, I cut straight to the storage hole, uncovering the foliage and wood planks without looking at him. I haul out my backpack and plastic bags and set it on the grass near his feet.

He stands like a tree in the center of the small clearing, scanning our surroundings. He points to his right where the grass is worn down.

"You slept there," he states.

"Uh huh," I acknowledge, beginning to sort through the few shirts that were ruined, throwing them in a bag for trash.

I hear whimpering. I look up to see Makono's face in his hands, his shoulders shaking. I scramble to my feet, stunned. "What—" but there is nothing to say, so I embrace him.

"No," he says, trying to shove me away, but I press him tighter against me. The sobs loosen from his body. He leans his head into my shoulder, surrendering. But even as I hold him, anger tightens in my gut. *How could he be so naive? It's a small thing, sleeping beneath the trees. It means nothing.*

Yet there is a smaller, much smaller voice that whispers *maybe he is not weeping for the imprint in the dirt but for the body of The Scream.* The one that hunted me like prey through the streets of Italy, that stalked me like sun through Spain. And here again it lies in the dirt, here it extends its hands, saying *see*.

Makono weeps because he sees. He sees what I myself can't bear to see—the way The Scream has hunted, has devoured, has distorted me. He borrows the weight of my tears until I am brave enough to hold them myself, until I am brave enough to release.

Inside my chest grows a new recitation:

maybe this means something

maybe this is the only meaningful thing

maybe Makono is the hero and I am just

an amoeba crawling back to the cold womb of the sea.

"Let's go," I whisper.

"Let's go," he repeats, wiping his eyes and shouldering the bag without looking at me.

He leads me through the bushes and I kick the jars accidentally, the blue skies and yellow fields spilling back into the earth.

Makono waits while I go to Sergi's apartment. This time he answers the door.

"I'm leaving," I say.

"When?" he asks.

"I go to Barcelona today. My flight leaves tomorrow."

"Oh." He shifts uncomfortably.

"I just came for my hat," I say, craning my neck to see the coat rack.

"Oh yes," he grabs it off the top, hands it to me.

"Well, if you ever come back..." he starts.

"Yeah, of course," I say, giving him a half-armed hug that feels colder than a handshake.

"Best of luck!" he calls out behind me, and I toss back a wave and a smile, already halfway to the cathedral, already thinking of home.

Standing outside the bus station, I turn to Makono. "Driver just texted. He's almost here."

He stands stiffly appraising me.

"I'm sorry that—" I begin.

"No," he shakes his head. "Can I...?" He extends his arms.

"Yes, yes," and I step towards him. His arms enfold me, my head resting easily against his chest for a few long heartbeats. "I'll—"

"Don't make any promises," he warns.

"I'll keep in touch."

"Yeah," he nods. "Me too."

The car pulls to the curb and Makono loads in my bags. I don't look back as we drive away. I'd rather not see his face as he watches me leave.

An hour later and I'm in Barcelona, hunting down Gaudí. I visit Casa Batlló and Park Güell, captivated by his architecture like an ecosystem of meaning, each building breathing. I pull out my notebook and begin recording:

Writing is secondary speech and speech is secondary Being. This Gaudi knew: that creation must be born of theophany (communion with the silence beneath beings and identities). He lived the authenticity that I seek.

I walk to a restaurant where I eat a slice of pizza, then sit on a bench to gather the last rays of Catalan sun, to soak up the last of the sky.

I will strip the world naked and re-language reality as if as if I were the first to blow dust from the book of the earth and say "breathe". I must re-translate the world through my life and re-write reality through my speech.

The next morning, I fly home.

The comfort of the plane makes my legs itch. I lean my forehead against the padded seat, my brain arching threateningly close to the architecture of my skull.

How delicately are these organs held inside.

I slide the pen into the spine and fall asleep. I awake near Los Angeles, the sprawling burnt lawns in patchwork patterns below. I stay awake for the next few hours, thrilling with excitement until we land.

Then I walk off the plane into the blinding heat and think: *Is this home?*

This plot is untied.

"I have to see you, David," I write.

I still don't have a phone, so we email back and forth. He has a dream that he is holding me, and "everything comes together, both of us finally home."

I am striding between rows of chairs, snatching up unused programs, handing them to an usher and unclipping my nametag. Then I run down the stairs until my heels make me totter, forcing me to speed walk instead.

Yes, be slow, be calm, I tell myself.

David and I agreed to meet in the university library's basement by a small gallery, the first time I will have seen him since I left.

Be slow, be calm.

I glance at the clock. Ten minutes to go. So I duck into a bathroom and pull the elastic from its bun, letting my hair cascade freely. I dab on a bit of lipstick, softening it with lip balm in hopes that it will look natural, that the redness won't reveal how desperately I still need him to want me.

Then I pace the length of the bathroom until an uncertain blonde pulls open the door. I smile uneasily and fling my backpack over my shoulder, pacing right past her. Out of the bathroom and into the study area, crossing the floor to the gallery. The gallery is carpeted and quiet, tucked away as an unfrequented afterthought. This year's exhibition is a series of collages, which I tilt my head to decipher until I hear footsteps approach.

I gasp before I even see his expectant smile, before I step into his arms and hold him tightly against me. He is three-dimensional! He is solid and warm. His sweater smells of a familiar cologne. I am *home*.

We don't speak for some long moments. I am struck once more by the brilliant blue of his eyes; they are searching my face as if deciphering the new space between us. *No space*, I decide. We are one, *just as if he were born with me, lived with me, and meant to take me to my grave.*

He suddenly laughs and pulls me to sit on a nearby bench. Our hands entwine effortlessly, and I hear him breathing.

"I—" I begin, not knowing where to lead us.

"You're wearing heels," he says.

I meet his eyes. "Oh, yes. Because I got a scholarship, and they make me help with these...speeches and events, that kind of thing."

"Wow."

I am looking at his shoes now, the leather loafers which approached *our bench* as I read. And I am smiling because they are practical and a little boring and yet they carried him to me once before and here they are again, a concrete symbol of his constancy.

"Congratulations," he adds, and I realize we are still talking about the scholarship, so I thank him.

"I…" Words trail off without me, my free hand moving to my forehead, which I rub anxiously. "I shouldn't have left. It was stupid, I should have stayed with you."

He presses my hand.

"I wasn't happy," I continued, "Not happy like I am with you."

He inhales deeply. Then he turns those eyes on me. "You won't leave again, will you?"

I look away, feel my palm beginning to sweat in his hand. "David, *how...*" My eyes are still fixed on those loafers, willing them to sprout roots. I nod. "I know I want to be with you. That's all I know."

I reach for his eyes with mine, and he seems satisfied.

"Good," he nods. And then he laughs, shaking his head, "You have no idea...no idea how I've missed you."

I kiss him. *All those men were stand-ins for him*, I think.

Hours pass in that basement as we resurrect our shared language of embraces, stories, and silences. "This is right," he whispers, while my head falls on his chest like those nights on New York subways.

And I think: *make me of this moment a material thing.*

We meet the next day, and the next, and we settle into a kind of peace.

He takes me to a park where we lay on a blanket beneath a tree whose leaves are changing. Gradually. The tips are just reddening, the centers losing their green. Between the leaves, a blue sky stuns with vibrancy.

It's laughing at me, I think.

But embarrassment kicks my gut immediately. *The earth doesn't speak and the sky doesn't laugh.* But if it did, would anyone hear it?

David's fingers brush my cheek. The blue of the sky still pulses behind my eyes as I see David's boring into mine. These eyes that hunted me through Europe, burned against my lids as I struggled with sleep, the eyes that see straight through me.

I close mine, breathing, as I slide my fingers over his face. And in my mind, I recite the lessons I learned in Spain: *Solitude is preparation for connection. Always, always it is about others in the end. The self is a starting point.*

As he holds me, I feel the vague sensation of "home" swell in my chest, threatening to take root–

I flinch.

I can't commit.

Later, I tell him this. He writes me beautiful letters as I begin dating other men. I buy a small chest from Amazon where I keep them carefully folded, waiting. With the letters inside, the chest begins to quiver with life, just like his name wandered through the streets of Spain, hungry as if searching for a page. I can't walk past the chest without feeling the ache, so I slide it under my bed.

In the winter, I make detours so I may pass by our bench a dozen times each week. Each time I expect him to re-appear, sitting patiently like a prelude to a new story. Each time I find it empty, crusted with cold or piled with snow. And an anger grips me: *damn the cosmic author we call destiny.*

When the cold thaws and the tulips climb brightly by the bench, he emails me. "I'm moving after graduation," he writes, "to take a job in D.C."

I go to his apartment to say goodbye. We sit on his couch and I interlace our fingers and then pull them apart, wondering at the strangeness of a hand disentangled from its source. What could my life be without knowing that somewhere on this planet, he is holding me?

"It was inevitable," I say, pontificating. "I love you more than I have ever loved anyone. But I can't see myself in D.C. with you, forever..."

This is true.

"And I can't see myself without you," he says.

This is also true. I can't imagine a life without him either, but now I know I will try.

"You were with me in Spain," I say, my throat tightening.

He is holding my hand between both of his, as if by holding it carefully enough, his warmth would stay imprinted on my hand. He doesn't look up, but I can tell he is listening by the tension of his body. He breathes into a pause. "I know," he says. His concentration does not break, and I feel the warmth pulsing into my palm like a gift.

We say goodbye, and I make my way to the underground garage beneath his apartment. I stand on a curb by a parked car before bending over, before sitting. *His love must be peeled from my skin*, I think. *Will there be anything but wound beneath?*

From the center of my stomach, I feel something tighten into a round, dark pit. "You have hollowed me out," I whisper.

Breathe.

I sit for a long stretch of time, focusing on that pain like an original point, like the early ache of displacement that explodes into the shape of our lives, like the fires which rage around us for the entirety of our days, threatening to swallow us blank. But as I wrap my breath around that original point, as I sink deeper and deeper into the loss, I feel a shiver like presence. I squint and imagine the pit splintering open. A spot of red at the center: is this joy?

Maybe pain is not the original point. Maybe it is freedom i.e. connection i.e. unbroken love i.e. the hum that rivers its way through the broken speech of being

i.e. *joy*.

At birth each child is dunked into this red sea. We emerge from the salt, soaked and rejoicing. Then, like Adam and Eve, we cover our nakedness with the skins of killed beasts. We mantle shame and suffering like second skins. We smother the innocence of original bodies.

But suffering *seen* can re-submerge us in this sea.

I press a hand against my stomach. *Meet the pain without blinking.*

We have all eaten of the fruit of life, not knowing we have swallowed its death-seeds. The seeds sprout into weeds tall as trees, choking. Smothered or not by distraction or belief, this we share: death as a shared feast, suffering as our communal drink.

Don't avert the gaze.

Through the languageless grief. Through the battering of The Scream. Until our feet redden with walking and our faces fray past expression. Only then can we press our knees into the communal sea, drinking. But the communal is connection, is healing. When we dunk our feet in its waters, the blood becomes wine and our wails collapse into laughter.

Breathe.

I put on my backpack and begin walking.

Soon I am in the university garden, where I sit on a bench. I take off my shoes and dig my toes into the damp soil beneath. Sprinklers, not rain, but the smell of the earth, at least. And I write:

*Nothing is lost here, in this place
before language, before longing.
The love is the same, after all.
Only the names change.*

But this red sea is no solution; it's only the beginning of a new way of healing.

*There is a wound shaped like a world
and it bears upon me like a tide.*

And the little girl is in it, and I listen for her scream. But as I strain to hear its pitch, its rhythm, its intensity, I realize I had never before listened so closely. As it loudens and loudens with proximity, my body tenses in surprise.

The sound is hollow.

Not unreal, but only a container. In the marrow rings a subtler note. An absence like a presence. An emptiness that expands. This note en-veined everything before the birth of selfhood severed us from the source. Like the stone which stared me down from beneath that tree, we all bear the marks of the sea, the ancient veins binding us from beneath.

This shared note will sing with or without my listening. But if I unmuffle it, maybe The Scream will stop pulsing behind my eyes, will become, instead, an opening.

*We enter the world through the wound.
The Scream opens the door to reality.*

The trees shiver with cold light. I dig my toes into the wet dirt as a pair of birds rustle from a branch, as they scatter into flight.

Breathe.

Epilogue

A year passes.

The semester has just ended, and the earth is slowly warming with spring.

I awake to the sun squeezing lemon-like through the blinds. This is not the sunshine of Spain, which roars open like a split tangerine, spilling into closed eyes. No. This sun is civilized, living safely behind my blinds.

Back in a warm apartment and couched in a comforting routine, it's easy to forget what nature does to those who seek her for more than a brief meditative remedy. Nature is a mother, which means she is the one who *rends*. She is the threat drawing us by shared blood again and again.

I go to my drawers and pull out a t-shirt and a pair of shorts. As I smell the faint whiff of detergent, I remember when I first came home, how I took out my clothes and laid them on the bed, lifting each piece to my nose and smelling it. The rapture soon passed. Clothing is ordinary; so is a bed.

My roommates are in the kitchen, eating cereal and chatting about the day ahead. "You wanna come to the water park?" the nice one asks.

I shake my head. "Thanks, though. I want to start my summer reading." The rude one smiles sweetly, "Wow, Sondra, you're *so smart*."

I smile all the way to my eyes, overcompensating for the tension. She must have been awake for awhile, because she has already attached her hair extensions, false lashes, and performed her entire bronzing and contouring routine.

"Have fun," I say, as they head out the door.

I stare at *A Critique of Pure Reason* for a few moments before opening it to my place, underlining a few lines, writing a few notes in the margins. After some dense pages and copious notes, I leave the book on the couch and open the closet for the sandals Makono gave me.

It's finally warm enough to wear them, and I smile at the buttery feel of good leather as I fasten them on my feet. I grab a canvas bag and a notebook and head outside, walking to the farmer's market. There I buy a bottle of goat's milk, a small jar of honey and a twine-tied bunch of dried chamomile. I place each carefully in the tote bag, aware that these are pretentious purchases for a college student living off a meager research fund.

I think of David, of course (I have never stopped thinking of David). I think of the many lives I would have to live before knowing how to love. I'm not sure what kind of creature love is, but I hope there is a species that is simply a foundation for my wanderings. Maybe real love is not fulfillment in another person, but the opening of a door. The security that allows you to step into the dangerous space of your own identity.

Someday, I will want someone who claims to love me.

I know this even now, as I take my bag to a bench and set it beside me, pulling out my notebook. I may even try on the word "home," exhale it like a mantra until it roots me in place, until it means something.

But whoever I choose, their love won't be enough to fill me.

I know that now. The love I want is like the curtain that never reached around the width of my body. Tossing and tossing and still cold each night. A thousand men could not keep me warm.

My soulmate is the totality of the teeming earth.

A shard of sky is caught in the goat's milk bottle, condensation gathering on the glass and sliding down the reflection of clouds like beads of rain. I reach into the bag and bring the chamomile to my nose, sifting through adjectives to describe. It's wild chamomile, so the scent is sharp, herbal, but there is a hint of sweetness, the suggestion of tea-coaxed dreams.

Love is a gathering of minutiae.

Stones, dirt particles, the waxing/waning light, goat's milk, chamomile, and honey. I am learning the excruciating art of attention, my small gift of sight to the world. The wider the world, the smaller I seem. This smallness is relieving. Concerns, like the self, are pebbles to be tossed into the sea.

When each noun is surrendered, the verb flows forth.

But these lines are not for pages. And they burst the bodies of words.

I close my eyes. I see that blurred blue horizon, the meeting place of sky and sea. *What lies on the other side of language?*

Maybe it's death.
Maybe it's peace.

We walk through an empty room until we see a light.

I rip out the page; I crumple it in my hand. I feel the paper pulsing in my fist as I walk.

Have I lived it? Have I lived it? Have I lived it?

The sky beats down, pacified.

Acknowledgments

To Catalonia, for tutoring me in art, history, and death.

To Makono.

To those dead muses—
Octavio Paz, Simone Weil, Wassily Kandinsky, Fyodor Dostoevsky, Rainer Maria Rilke, Albert Camus, Joan Miró, Walt Whitman—
dead, but still speaking.

To my editors, John Knight and Dionne McCulloch, who offered exactly the feedback and encouragement I needed.

To Christian, for being a spiritual mentor and my first reader. To Marybeth, for your loyalty, love, and excitement for life. To Victoria, for your insight and infectious goodness (and for being the first to buy a copy of this book!).

To my husband, Georg, for the devoted love and constant laughter, and for helping make this book a reality. To my daughter, who makes everything mean something.

And to you, reader. It means the world that you have accompanied me on this journey.

Thank you.

Thank you.

Thank you.

Author Bio

Sondra lives with her husband and daughter in the American West. To read more of her writing, you can visit her website at www.sondrawriter.com and sign up for her mailing list. And if you enjoyed this book, please support indie authors by sharing it with a friend and leaving a review wherever you bought it.

www.ingramcontent.com/pod-product-compliance
Lightning Source LLC
Chambersburg PA
CBHW072154100526
44589CB00015B/2224